Vocabulary Workshop

with iWords™  Audio Program

Common Core Enriched Edition

Jerome Shostak

Consultants

Joseph Czarnecki, Ph.D.
Faculty Associate, School of Education
Johns Hopkins University
Baltimore, MD

Christine Gialamas-Antonucci
Reading Specialist
Chicago Public Schools
Chicago, IL

Lucy Lugones
Technology Consultant
St. Luke's School
New York, NY

Helen Wood Turner, Ed.D.
Reading Specialist
Turning Point Academy
Lanham, MD

S Sadlier

Level Blue

Vocabulary Workshop

with iWords™ Audio Program

C Common Core Enriched Edition

Advisers

The publisher wishes to thank the following teachers and administrators, who read portions of the series prior to publication, for their comments and suggestions.

Carolyn Branch
Lead Charter Administrator
Kansas City, MO

Khawla Asmar
Assistant Principal
Milwaukee, WI

Tara M. Gaiss
Literacy Specialist
Kings Park, NY

Amy Cristina
Teacher
Panama City, FL

Ann Jennings
English Specialist
Rustburg, VA

Lisa Mayer
Teacher
Houston, TX

Cora M. Kirby
Reading Specialist
Washington, DC

Megan Mayfield
Teacher
Woodstock, GA

Nancy Wahl
Elementary School Teacher
New York, NY

Julie Cambonga
Assistant Principal/Teacher
Sierra Madre, CA

Photo Credits: Cover: pencil: Used under license from Shutterstock.com/Pedro Nogueria; wood grain on pencil: Used under license from Shutterstock.com/Christophe Testi. Interior: Alamy/Nigel Cattlin: 99 *left*; image100 Sports H: 88–89; First Light/Peter Reali: 27 *left*; Louise A. Heusinkveld: 98–99; Mary Evans Picture Library: 56; Jim M. McDonald: 48; moodboard: 111; North Wind Picture Archives: 181 *left*; Pictorial Press Ltd: 130 *left*; SusivoutiStock: 108; Ted Foxx: 132. Animals Animals/Earth Scenes/Patti Murray: 26–27. AP Photo/Damian Dovarganes: 71. The Bridgeman Art Library/Bibliotheque des Arts Decoratifs, Paris, France/Archives Charmet/Troop of mammoths in the Ice Age (colour litho) by Wilhelm Kuhnert (1865-1923) (after): 160–161; © Staatliche Kunstsammlungen Dresden/Jupiter and Mercury in the House of Philemon and Baucis (oil on copper) by Adam Elsheimer (1578-1610) Gemaeldegalerie Alte Meister, Dresden, Germany: 46. Corbis/Bettmann: 36–37, 57, 79, 80, 140 *bottom*, 158, 172, 188; DPA: 58; Danny Lehman: 27 *right*; McKim, Mead and White: 78; Naturbild/Kentaroo Tryman: 121 left; Reuters/Christinne Muschi: 18; John L. Simbert: 130 *right*; Ariel Skelley: 101. Dreamstime/Martin Allinger: 183 *top*; Cheeonn Leon: 8; Vassiliy Mikhailin: 29; Monkey Business Images: 81; Catalin Petolea: 140–141; Patrick Poendl: 173; Micha Rosenwirth: 64; Danny Warren: 28; Ivonne Wierink: 89. Everett Collection: 19. Fotolia/Kenny Stuck: 183 *bottom*. The Granger Collection, New York: 34, 37, 98, 99 *right*. Getty Images/AFP/Therence Koh: 142; AFP/Brendan Smialowski: 9; DEA Picture Library: 170 *top*; Digital Vision/Compassionate Eye Foundation/Rob Daly/OJO Images Ltd: 49; Getty Images News/Mario Tama: 90 *bottom*; Hulton Archive: 96 *background*; National Geographic/Walter Meayers Edwards: 126; Nativestock.com/Marilyn Angel Wynn: 181 right; Panoramic Images: 161; Realistic Reflections: 70; Riser/Bob Elsdale: 152; Stone/Bruce Foster: 110; Stone/Michael Rosenfeld: 133. iStockphoto/Pierre-Yves Babelon: 59; Christophe Boisson: 158 *background*; karlkotasinc: 143 *bottom*; luoman: 96 *background*. The Library of Congress: 180. National Geographic Stock/David Doubilet: 69. New York State Historical Association Research Library, Cooperstown, NY/The Farmer's Museum: 140 *top*, 141. North Wind Picture Archives: 16–17, 143 *top*. PhotoEdit, Inc./Susan Van Etten: 121 *bottom*. Photographers Direct/Darlene Bordwell: 17. Punchstock/Comstock Images: 108–109; Panoramic Images: 153. robertstock.com: 39. Used under license from Shutterstock.com/akva: 131; Alperium: 118–119; Mohamed Farouk Badawi: 47; Liem Bahneman: 90 *top*; Goldenangel: 163 *bottom*; Michael Pettigrew: 38; tonobalaguerf: 118. Smithsonian/National Postal Museum: 16. SuperStock/Image Source: 100. University of Maryland/John Consoli: 68.

Illustrators: Monica Armino: 170, 171. Jared Beckstrand: 8, 10, 28, 30, 49, 50, 58, 60, 120, 122, 162, 164. David Neale: 006–007. Tim Raglin: 150–151. Chris Vallo: 18, 20, 39, 40, 71, 72, 81, 82, 91, 92, 100, 102, 110, 112, 132, 134, 143, 144, 153, 154, 172, 174, 182, 184.

For additional online resources, go to **vocabularyworkshop.com** and enter the Student Access Code VWL11S9FBQT4.

S® is a registered trademark of William H. Sadlier, Inc.

Printed in the United States of America.
ISBN: 978-0-8215-8005-9
456789 BRR 16 15 14 13

Note to the Student

Most of the vocabulary words in **Level Blue** will be new to you. Some words you may recognize. Others you may not know at all. The words have been chosen because they are words you will come across often. You will see them in schoolbooks and on tests. You will see them in books and magazines, as well as on the Internet. You will also hear them spoken by teachers and others in a variety of professions.

In each of the 18 units, you will read a passage that contains the 12 unit words. You will see and hear how the words are used in the passage. Then you will learn more about them, including their definitions, pronunciations, parts of speech, and how they are used in sentences. You will also find synonyms and antonyms for the words. As you complete the pages in the unit, not only will you practice using the words, but you will also show what you know about them.

Each unit also helps you build vocabulary beyond the unit words. For example, in **Word Study**, you will learn how to use word parts (prefixes, suffixes, roots) to figure out the meanings of unfamiliar words. In **Shades of Meaning**, you will learn the meanings of some idioms, proverbs, similes, and metaphors.

When you finish this book, your vocabulary will have grown. All the words you have learned will be part of your personal vocabulary, helping you to become a better reader, writer, and speaker.

Interactive Online Activities

Don't forget to look at the online activities that extend and enrich the instruction and practice contained in **Level Blue**. Access to these free activities and more is available at **vocabularyworkshop.com**.

Contents

Introducing the Words

Read the following Russian folktale about some clever forest animals. Notice how the highlighted words are used. These are the words you will be learning in this unit.

Why Bear Sleeps So Much

(Russian Folktale)

Long ago, when the world was as fresh and new as a daffodil in springtime, the animals faced a serious problem. Troublesome Bear was ruining everything in their forest.

The songbirds were all terrified whenever Bear passed through the woods in his usual clumsy way. He would blunder into branches, smashing the birds' fragile nests and eggs. Bear also crushed the hives of the bees and stole their honey, so the bees had a continuous argument with him. Bear squashed the tunnel-like homes of the gophers and the rabbits with his big feet, and in general caused so many disturbances that the animals couldn't relax. As angry as they were, however, the animals didn't really want to get into a scuffle with Bear. He was much too big and strong!

Desperate, the animals called a meeting to decide on a course of action. "Why don't we just ask Bear to be more considerate?" suggested Deer timidly.

Squirrel was quick to reject Deer's idea. "That won't work," Squirrel insisted, "because Bear never listens to anyone. I think he just enjoys walking all over us!"

"Throw Bear in jail," Rat shouted. "Force him to live a solitary life in a jail cell and he won't be able to injure and torment us ever again."

The animals nodded in approval at this idea until Mouse pointed out an obvious problem. "We don't have a jail," Mouse squeaked, "and if we did, someone would have to feed Bear in his cell." The very thought of feeding Bear made all the animals shake in fear.

Other animals offered more ideas. Skunk suggested that Porcupine distribute some of his extra sharp quills in Bear's bed. Porcupine suggested that Skunk send some smelly spray into Bear's den. Neither animal was brave enough to try the other's plan, however, and the ideas probably wouldn't have worked anyway. Indeed, it looked as if there were no solution to the problem, and the animals were about to cancel the rest of their meeting.

Fortunately, at that moment, Eagle flew in like a bolt of lightning. The animals cheered because Eagle was a veteran problem solver. Whenever there was trouble in the forest, Eagle found a way to put an end to it. This time, Eagle clutched a document in his sharp claws. "As we all know," Eagle thundered, "Bear can't hurt anyone or destroy anything when he's asleep. This statement," he said, waving the document, "requires Bear to sleep from October to April every year. I hope you will all sign it!"

What a great idea! The animals read the document and added their names to it. True, it didn't get rid of Bear permanently, but it gave them temporary relief. At the very least, the animals could look forward to peace and quiet for six months of every year.

The myth doesn't say how the animals gave their signed document to Bear or what his reaction was to it. Who knows? Maybe he liked the animals' suggestion, for one thing is certain: Bear has been sleeping away half the year ever since!

Definitions

You were introduced to the words below in the passage on pages 6–7. Study the pronunciation, spelling, part of speech, and definition of each word. Write the word in the blank space in the sentence that follows. Then read the synonyms and antonyms.

1. blunder
(blun′ dər)

(v.) to make a foolish or careless mistake; to move clumsily and carelessly

I saw the hiker _____ through the woods.

(n.) a serious or thoughtless mistake

I was terribly embarrassed by my _____.

SYNONYMS: (v.) to err, foul up, bungle, goof; (n.) an error, blooper
ANTONYMS: (v.) to triumph, succeed; (n.) a success, hit

2. cancel
(kan′ səl)

(v.) to call off or do away with; to cross out with lines or other marks to show that something cannot be used again

Maybe the principal will _____ classes if it continues to snow.

SYNONYMS: to stop, discontinue, drop, repeal, revoke
ANTONYMS: to renew, continue, extend, maintain

3. continuous
(kən tin′ yü əs)

(adj.) going on without a stop or break

_____ TV coverage began shortly after news of the disaster broke.

SYNONYMS: ongoing, endless, ceaseless, unbroken, constant, perpetual
ANTONYMS: broken, discontinuous, interrupted

4. distribute
(di stri′ byüt)

(v.) to give out in shares; to scatter or spread

Our class will _____ leaflets announcing the school's fund-raising drive.

SYNONYMS: to divide, share, deal, issue
ANTONYMS: to gather, collect, hold

5. document
(dä′ kyə ment)

(n.) a written or printed record that gives information or proof

The librarian found the old _____ inside a book.

(v.) to give written or printed proof; to support with evidence

Writers often _____ their sources.

SYNONYMS: (n.) a certificate, deed; (v.) to prove, establish

6. fragile
(fra' jəl)

(adj.) easily broken or damaged, requiring special handling or care

The _____ *antique was damaged during transit.*

SYNONYMS: weak, frail, breakable, delicate, brittle, flimsy
ANTONYMS: sturdy, hardy, strong, rugged, tough

7. myth
(mith)

(n.) an old story that explains why something is or how it came to be; something imaginary

The play is based on an ancient Greek _____.

SYNONYMS: a legend, fable, tale, fantasy, fairy tale
ANTONYM: a fact

8. reject
(ri jekt')

(v.) to refuse to accept, agree to, believe, or use

Why did you _____ *the offer?*

SYNONYMS: to deny, discard, junk, scrap, decline, dismiss
ANTONYMS: to take, accept, receive, welcome

9. scuffle
(sku' fəl)

(v.) to fight or struggle closely with

A witness saw the two men _____ *in an alley.*

(n.) fight or struggle

Police officers were called in to break up the _____.

SYNONYMS: (v.) to tussle, roughhouse, battle, brawl; (n.) a fistfight, clash

10. solitary
(sä' lə ter ē)

(adj.) living or being alone; being the only one

The old man led a _____ *life.*

SYNONYMS: single, sole, lone
ANTONYMS: sociable; several, many, numerous

11. temporary
(tem' pə rer ē)

(adj.) lasting or used for a limited time

A blow to the head can cause a _____ *loss of memory.*

SYNONYMS: short-term, passing, brief, momentary
ANTONYMS: lasting, long-lived, permanent

12. veteran
(ve' tə rən)

(n.) a former member of the armed forces; an experienced person

The army _____ *listened attentively.*

(adj.) having much experience in some job or field

The actress will play a _____ *reporter.*

SYNONYMS: (adj.) expert, professional, experienced, skilled, accomplished
ANTONYMS: (n.) a beginner, newcomer, novice, rookie

Match the Meaning

vocabularyworkshop.com **Practice** unit words with interactive games and activities.

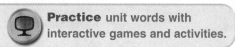

For each item below, choose the word whose meaning is suggested by the clue given. Then write the word in the space provided.

1. A roommate you have for only a month is a _____ one.
   a. continuous   b. temporary   c. fragile   d. solitary

2. A black eye might be the result of a _____.
   a. scuffle   b. myth   c. veteran   d. blunder

3. To _____ your age you might show a birth certificate or a driver's license.
   a. distribute   b. document   c. cancel   d. reject

4. A person who lives alone in the woods might be described as

   _____.
   a. continuous   b. solitary   c. temporary   d. fragile

5. The idea that you will get warts from touching a frog is a

   _____.
   a. blunder   b. document   c. scuffle   d. myth

6. If I make a serious mistake, I commit a _____.
   a. scuffle   b. document   c. myth   d. blunder

7. A box containing an item that can be broken easily might be

   stamped "_____."
   a. solitary   b. temporary   c. fragile   d. continuous

8. A charity might _____ food to the homeless.
   a. reject   b. cancel   c. scuffle   d. distribute

9. Something that goes on without stopping is _____.
   a. continuous   b. temporary   c. solitary   d. fragile

10. To refuse a gift is to _____ it.
   a. cancel   b. scuffle   c. distribute   d. reject

11. A person who has a lot of experience at something is a _____.
   a. blunder   b. myth   c. document   d. veteran

12. If I call off a party, I _____ it.
   a. scuffle   b. blunder   c. cancel   d. reject

The dog and cat got into a scuffle.

Synonyms

*For each item below, choose the word that is most nearly the **same** in meaning as the word or phrase in **boldface**. Then write your choice on the line provided.*

1. a **constant** flow of traffic
   a. fragile   b. temporary   c. continuous   d. veteran   _____

2. tried to hide the **blooper**
   a. document   b. myth   c. blunder   d. scuffle   _____

3. not a **single** cent
   a. temporary   b. fragile   c. solitary   d. veteran   _____

4. witnessed the **fight**
   a. myth   b. blunder   c. document   d. scuffle   _____

5. very important **records**
   a. veterans   b. documents   c. myths   d. blunders   _____

6. a collection of ancient **stories**
   a. documents   b. myths   c. veterans   d. blunders   _____

Antonyms

*For each item below, choose the word that is most nearly **opposite** in meaning to the word or phrase in **boldface**. Then write your choice on the line provided.*

1. **renew** my subscription
   a. cancel   b. blunder   c. scuffle   d. distribute   _____

2. **accept** the marriage proposal
   a. scuffle   b. reject   c. blunder   d. distribute   _____

3. a **novice** mountain climber
   a. temporary   b. fragile   c. continuous   d. veteran   _____

4. **collect** the homework sheets
   a. reject   b. document   c. distribute   d. cancel   _____

5. a **sturdy** device
   a. temporary   b. solitary   c. veteran   d. fragile   _____

6. a **permanent** filling
   a. veteran   b. continuous   c. temporary   d. solitary   _____

Completing the Sentence

Choose the word from the box that best completes each item below. Then write the word in the space provided. (You may have to change the word's ending.)

blunder	cancel	continuous
distribute	document	fragile
myth	reject	scuffle
solitary	temporary	veteran

A Visit to a Museum

■ Our class visited the museum on the last day of a(n) _____ exhibit of ancient Greek vases.

■ Some of the vases were more than 2,000 years old. Because they were so old and

_____, we weren't allowed to touch them.

■ Security guards kept visitors a few feet from the display cases, so there was no chance

that someone could _____ into them.

■ The guide told us that the pictures painted on some of the vases were not of real

people but characters from legends and _____.

■ One picture showed a(n) _____ warrior fighting off a band of attackers.

A Famous Declaration

■ In refusing to accept English rule, the writers of the Declaration of Independence

_____ the claim that Parliament had sovereignty, or lawful power, over the American colonies.

■ Those who supported the cause of American independence quickly printed and

_____ copies of the Declaration throughout the thirteen colonies.

■ The original _____, one of America's historic treasures, is now on view at the National Archives building in Washington, D.C.

On the Soccer Field

■ Two days of _____ rain had turned the soccer field into a sea of mud and threatened to spoil the opening game of the season.

■ Before the game began, a _____ broke out in the stands when a few home-team fans came to blows with those rooting for the visiting team.

■ The referee threatened to _____ the game and send all of the fans home if order was not restored.

■ Only when a handful of popular _____ from both teams asked the fans to behave themselves did they finally settle down and let the game get under way.

Word Associations

*Circle the letter next to the word or expression that best completes the sentence or answers the question. Pay special attention to the word in **boldface**.*

1. A person might emerge from a **scuffle**
   a. with spaghetti and meatballs.
   b. with scrapes and bruises.
   c. with dollars and cents.
   d. with hugs and kisses.

2. Someone who has **blundered** would
   a. feel embarrassed.
   b. be confident.
   c. feel proud.
   d. be rewarded.

3. A **solitary** tree would probably
   a. have needles.
   b. be chopped down.
   c. change color in the fall.
   d. stand alone.

4. A **continuous** loud noise might
   a. be hard to hear.
   b. stop and start.
   c. be soothing.
   d. be annoying.

5. Which of the following is a **document**?
   a. an old friend
   b. a telephone call
   c. a marriage license
   d. a good meal

6. If I **cancel** my piano lesson,
   a. I don't go.
   b. I play very well.
   c. I repair the piano.
   d. I arrive late.

7. A **temporary** problem is one that
   a. lasts a long time.
   b. goes away.
   c. no one can solve.
   d. anyone can solve.

8. In a **veteran's** closet you might find
   a. a skateboard.
   b. a party dress.
   c. a box of marbles.
   d. an old uniform.

9. When a teacher **distributes** a test
   a. he or she grades it.
   b. he or she loses it.
   c. he or she passes it out.
   d. he or she collects it.

10. Which of the following is usually **fragile**?
   a. a hammer
   b. a pair of scissors
   c. a lightbulb
   d. a padlock

11. Someone who has been **rejected**
   a. might feel hurt.
   b. might feel happy.
   c. might get lost.
   d. might get a cold.

12. Which is a creature of **myth**?
   a. a rabbit
   b. a giraffe
   c. a duck
   d. a dragon

Word Study • Dictionary: Multiple-Meaning Words 1

A **multiple-meaning word** is a word with more than one meaning. One example from this unit is *veteran* (page 9). If you look up *veteran* in a dictionary, you will find an entry with numbers showing the word's different meanings.

veteran 1. *(n.)* a person who has served in the armed forces: *My father is a Gulf War veteran.* **2.** *(n.)* a person who has a lot of experience: *The respected soccer player is a veteran of his sport.*

Read this sentence: *My favorite baseball player was a ten-year veteran of the team.* You can tell from the definitions that the sentence illustrates meaning 2 of *veteran*.

Look at the chart to find other examples of multiple-meaning words.

coat	**1.** *(n.)* an item of clothing worn when it is cold **2.** *(v.)* to cover a surface with something
drill	**1.** *(n.)* a safety routine **2.** *(n.)* a tool used to make holes in hard surfaces
uniform	**1.** *(n.)* an outfit worn by members of a group **2.** *(adj.)* hardly any or no difference

PRACTICE *Write the multiple-meaning word from the chart above that completes each sentence. Using the part of speech can help you choose the word. Then write the number of the meaning.*

_____ **1.** Be sure to put on your _____ before you go out in the snow.

_____ **2.** Our classroom is kept at a _____ temperature.

_____ **3.** Our school has a fire _____ at least once a month.

_____ **4.** The cook will _____ the pan with oil so the onions don't stick.

APPLY *Complete each sentence so that it makes sense. Use the multiple-meaning word in **boldface**. You may have to change the word's ending.*

5. drill To hang the picture, we _____.

6. coat The floor will look shiny and new if I _____.

7. uniform To show that we are members of the glee club, we _____.

8. veteran After teaching for twenty-four years, the teacher _____.

Speak *Think of the multiple meanings for each word below. Then use one of the words in a sentence. Ask your partner to tell what the word means.*

light *(n.)* / **light** *(v.)*   **bend** *(n.)* / **bend** *(v.)*

Shades of Meaning • Similes

In the passage "Why Bear Sleeps So Much" on pages 6–7, you read this sentence: *Fortunately, at that moment, Eagle flew in **like a bolt of lightning**.* In this sentence, *like a bolt of lightning* is a simile.

A **simile** compares two unlike things using the word *like* or *as*. In the sentence from the passage, the simile *like a bolt of lightning* compares the way Eagle flew to a bolt of lightning. Since a bolt of lightning is known for how quickly it can strike, saying that Eagle flew like a bolt of lightning means that Eagle flew very quickly.

PRACTICE *Complete each sentence with a simile at the right. Write the number of the sentence next to the simile.*

1. The sisters are identical twins. They are _____.   ____ like cats and dogs.

2. My brother and I can never agree on anything. Our   ____ like two peas in a pod.

   parents say that we fight _____.   ____ as rough as sandpaper.

3. I am very talkative, but my best friend is _____.   ____ as quiet as a mouse.

4. The gardener's dry, chapped hands are _____.

APPLY *Complete each sentence so that it makes sense. Pay attention to the simile in **boldface**.*

5. When I am **as hungry as a bear**, I _____

   _____.

6. I think my grandmother is **as sweet as honey** because _____

   _____.

7. The student driver looked **like a deer caught in the headlights** when _____

   _____.

8. After gym, I moved **like a snail** because _____

   _____.

9. I felt **like a fish out of water** during my first _____

   _____.

Introducing the Words

Read the following historical nonfiction passage about a hero of the American Revolution. Notice how the highlighted words are used. These are the words you will be learning in this unit.

Sybil Ludington's Ride
(Historical Nonfiction)

Listen my children and you shall hear of the midnight ride of . . . Sybil Ludington? Thanks to a very famous poem, almost everyone knows about Paul Revere. The name of Sybil Ludington, however, is probably unfamiliar. Yet like Revere, Ludington made an impressive midnight ride to warn American patriots—those fighting for independence—of an approaching British army.

In April 1777, two years after Revere's famous ride, British soldiers made an assault on Danbury, Connecticut, not too far from where sixteen-year-old Sybil Ludington lived. The Continental Army, as the army of the Americans was called, stored supplies in Danbury, and the British strategy was to burn them. Once the supplies were destroyed, the British began to burn the homes and workplaces of numerous patriots in Danbury. The villain in this raid was the British general William Tryon, who lost control of his soldiers and allowed them to hurt innocent citizens.

A messenger quickly rode out from Danbury with news of the attack. His destination was the mill of Colonel Henry Ludington in nearby New York State. Only Ludington, the leader of about four hundred patriot volunteers, could fight off the British. After hearing the news, Ludington quickly agreed to help, but his men were spread out for miles. Who would alert them?

This postage stamp honors Sybil Ludington's contribution to the cause of American freedom.

The messenger from Danbury did not know his way around the area. Ludington himself had to stay at home to assemble his soldiers as they arrived. Perhaps that's when Ludington's daughter Sybil volunteered to make the ride, or perhaps Ludington asked her to go. Either way, it was a shrewd choice. No one could dispute that Sybil was a skillful rider, and she knew the local roads well. Also, as the oldest of twelve children, she was used to responsibility. Sending Sybil was a decision that would be easy to justify.

Sybil quickly mounted her horse and rode off on her mission. It was after 9:00 P.M. and raining when she left, and in the darkness, the rough unmarked trails could be misleading. Sybil never lost her way though, galloping from farm to village and calling out the news. In all, she rode forty miles that night, twice as far as Paul Revere. Along the way, she had to avoid British spies and soldiers. According to one account, she even used a type of gun called a musket to scare away some outlaws who preyed on travelers at night.

Sybil had a productive ride that night! When she arrived back home at dawn, more than four hundred patriot volunteers were gathering at her father's mill. Under Colonel Ludington, they were quickly converted into a regular fighting force. By now, the British had burned and abandoned Danbury and were marching inland. Ludington's forces, however, stopped the British advance. Later, at the Battle of Ridgefield, the patriots fought the British invaders, who eventually retreated to their boats on Long Island Sound.

In the months that followed, Sybil's father and the volunteers he led often praised and thanked Sybil for her heroic ride. Even General George Washington sent his congratulations for a job well done. Like so many other patriots, Sybil Ludington had come to the aid of her country.

Definitions

You were introduced to the words below in the passage on pages 16–17. Study the pronunciation, spelling, part of speech, and definition of each word. Write the word in the blank space in the sentence that follows. Then read the synonyms and antonyms.

1. **abandon**
   (ə ban' dən)

   (v.) to give up on completely; to leave with no intention of returning

   The captain gave the order to _____ ship.

   SYNONYMS: to desert, forsake, cease, surrender
   ANTONYMS: to continue, stay, remain, occupy

2. **assault**
   (ə sôlt')

   (n.) a violent attack

   The victim was injured in the _____.

   (v.) to attack violently or suddenly

   Dad dared us to _____ his snow fort.

   SYNONYMS: (n.) an invasion, raid, mugging, beating; (v.) to besiege, storm
   ANTONYMS: (v.) to protect, defend, resist

3. **convert**
   (v., kən vûrt';
   n., kän' vûrt)

   (v.) to change from one form to another

   A drop in temperature to 32° F will _____ water to ice.

   (n.) a person who has changed from one opinion, belief, or religion to another

   The new _____ was introduced to the congregation.

   SYNONYMS: (v.) to transform, turn, alter, switch
   ANTONYMS: (v.) to maintain, conserve, remain

4. **dispute**
   (di spyüt')

   (v.) to argue, debate, quarrel over; to question or doubt the truth of

   The committee did not _____ the merits of the bill.

   (n.) an argument, quarrel, debate

   Why not try to resolve the _____ peacefully?

   SYNONYMS: (v.) to differ, disagree; contest, challenge; (n.) a conflict, disagreement, controversy
   ANTONYMS: (v.) to agree, harmonize; (n.) an agreement, understanding, accord

5. **impressive**
   (im pre' siv)

   (adj.) having a strong effect, commanding attention

   The skater gave an _____ performance.

   SYNONYMS: memorable, striking, stirring, thrilling, awesome, splendid
   ANTONYMS: inferior, mediocre

6. justify
(jus′ tə fī)

(v.) to show to be fair or right; to give good reasons for

Be prepared to _____ your behavior.

SYNONYMS: to defend, explain, support, excuse
ANTONYMS: to convict, blame, accuse

7. misleading
(mis lē′ diŋ)

(adj.) tending to give a wrong idea, often on purpose

The lawyer called the statement _____.

SYNONYMS: deceptive, false, tricky, inaccurate
ANTONYMS: direct, honest, true, accurate, straightforward

8. numerous
(nüm′ rəs)

(adj.) many or very many

_____ aunts and uncles came to our family reunion.

SYNONYMS: several, plenty, plentiful
ANTONYM: few

9. productive
(prə duk′ tiv)

(adj.) making or capable of making large amounts of; giving good results

With care, it may become a _____ orchard.

SYNONYMS: energetic, effective, fruitful, efficient, worthwhile
ANTONYMS: unproductive, idle, useless, inactive

10. shrewd
(shrüd)

(adj.) showing clever judgment and practical understanding

My aunt is a _____ businesswoman.

SYNONYMS: artful, wise, sharp, crafty, wily, cunning
ANTONYMS: slow, stupid, dull-witted

11. strategy
(stra′ tə jē)

(n.) a carefully made plan or plot; a plan of military operations

Our teacher suggested a test-taking _____.

SYNONYMS: an approach, design, method, scheme

12. villain
(vi′ lən)

(n.) an evil or wicked person or character, especially in a story or play

In old movies, the _____ often wore a black hat.

SYNONYMS: a scoundrel, rascal, outlaw, criminal
ANTONYMS: a hero, heroine, champion

Match the Meaning

 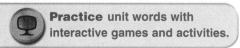

For each item below, choose the word whose meaning is suggested by the clue given. Then write the word in the space provided.

1. A violent or sudden attack is called a(n) _____.
   a. convert   b. assault   c. strategy   d. villain

2. When I carefully make a plan, I am preparing my _____.
   a. strategy   b. dispute   c. villain   d. convert

3. People who change their religion are _____ to the new religion.
   a. disputes   b. converts   c. strategies   d. villains

4. To give reasons for what you do is to _____ your actions.
   a. justify   b. abandon   c. assault   d. convert

5. Some advertisements can be _____ if they leave out key details or make false claims.
   a. misleading   b. numerous   c. productive   d. impressive

6. The most wicked character in the story is the _____.
   a. assault   b. strategy   c. villain   d. dispute

7. A vegetarian cookbook might give _____ recipes for rice dishes and fruit salads.
   a. productive   b. shrewd   c. misleading   d. numerous

8. To give up on something is to _____ it.
   a. assault   b. abandon   c. convert   d. justify

9. Another word for an argument or quarrel is a _____.
   a. convert   b. strategy   c. villain   d. dispute

10. A(n) _____ person is one who gets a lot done.
   a. productive   b. shrewd   c. misleading   d. impressive

11. The Grand Canyon is a(n) _____ sight.
   a. shrewd   b. misleading   c. impressive   d. numerous

12. To be clever and practical is to be _____.
   a. misleading   b. shrewd   c. productive   d. numerous

At half-time, the team developed a **strategy** for winning the game.

Synonyms

*For each item below, choose the word that is most nearly the **same** in meaning as the word or phrase in **boldface**. Then write your choice on the line provided.*

1. change starch to sugar
a. abandon   b. assault   c. dispute   d. convert   _____

2. supported the decision
a. abandoned   b. assaulted   c. justified   d. converted   _____

3. a **thrilling** performance
a. misleading   b. numerous   c. shrewd   d. impressive   _____

4. tried to be more **effective**
a. numerous   b. misleading   c. productive   d. shrewd   _____

5. a problem-solving **approach**
a. strategy   b. assault   c. dispute   d. villain   _____

6. a **crafty** move
a. misleading   b. impressive   c. shrewd   d. productive   _____

Antonyms

*For each item below, choose the word that is most nearly **opposite** in meaning to the word or phrase in **boldface**. Then write your choice on the line provided.*

1. agreed with the umpire's call
a. disputed   b. assaulted   c. converted   d. justified   _____

2. few paint colors
a. shrewd   b. misleading   c. numerous   d. productive   _____

3. occupy the old shack
a. assault   b. convert   c. abandon   d. justify   _____

4. defended the bridge
a. converted   b. assaulted   c. disputed   d. justified   _____

5. the **hero** of the movie
a. convert   b. assault   c. strategy   d. villain   _____

6. gave **accurate** directions to the tourist
a. impressive   b. misleading   c. numerous   d. productive   _____

Completing the Sentence

Choose the word from the box that best completes each item below. Then write the word in the space provided. (You may have to change the word's ending.)

abandon	assault	convert
dispute	impressive	justify
misleading	numerous	productive
shrewd	strategy	villain

Greeks and Trojans at War

■ Both the Greek poet Homer and the Roman poet Virgil wrote of the ten-year siege of Troy by the Greeks and of the heroes and _____ who did battle there.

■ One of the most famous stories describes the sly _____ that the Greeks thought up to defeat the Trojans.

■ The Greeks had tried not once but on _____ occasions to force the Trojans to surrender the fortress city.

■ Several times the Greeks had _____ the walls of Troy, but all of the attacks had failed.

■ Finally, the Greeks came up with a _____ plan: They left at the gates of Troy a huge wooden horse as a pretended peace offering. The Trojans brought the horse inside the city walls.

■ But the wooden horse was a _____ gift, for hidden inside its huge body was a small army of Greeks, who at nightfall climbed from the horse and opened the gates to the city.

A False Science

■ Alchemists were people who believed that it was possible to _____ ordinary metals, such as iron and lead, into gold. The best-known alchemists are those who practiced in Europe during the Middle Ages.

■ They staged very _____ experiments to try to convince others that they could do as they promised.

■ Some people believed that the possibility of great wealth _____ even the most far-fetched experiments.

■ Scientists today would _____ the ideas of the alchemists, but centuries ago many people believed that their ideas were sound. In fact, it was not until the 1800s that scientists proved that base metals cannot be turned into gold.

■ Failure upon failure finally persuaded most alchemists to _____ their dreams of wealth and glory.

■ In a way, the work that the alchemists did was _____ because it sometimes led to advances in chemistry. During the Middle Ages, for example, alchemists were responsible for the discovery of mineral acids.

Word Associations

*Circle the letter next to the word or expression that best completes the sentence or answers the question. Pay special attention to the word in **boldface**.*

1. A person who has been **abandoned**
   a. would feel powerful.
   b. would feel bold.
   c. would feel happy.
   d. would feel lonely.

2. If you **convert** a room, you
   a. leave it the same.
   b. hide in it.
   c. change it.
   d. take a picture of it.

3. You might expect a **villain** to
   a. volunteer in a soup kitchen.
   b. receive an award.
   c. play the cello.
   d. kidnap someone.

4. A really **impressive** baseball team would
   a. use extra players.
   b. lack the proper equipment.
   c. lead the league.
   d. play only night games.

5. Which might stop an **assault**?
   a. a good night's sleep
   b. a police officer
   c. a salt shaker
   d. a rocking horse

6. A winning **strategy** involves
   a. careful planning.
   b. lots of money.
   c. powerful friends.
   d. reckless bravery.

7. On a **productive** day you would
   a. play outside.
   b. get a lot done.
   c. stay inside.
   d. get nothing done.

8. If your friends are **numerous,**
   a. you have very few of them.
   b. they live nearby.
   c. you have a lot of them.
   d. they live far away.

9. Misleading information should usually be
   a. ignored.
   b. memorized.
   c. published.
   d. relied upon.

10. When I **justify** my claims,
   a. I take them back.
   b. I lose them.
   c. I defend them.
   d. I get sued.

11. A **shrewd** person would probably
   a. get lost.
   b. get a good deal.
   c. get a warm welcome.
   d. get fooled.

12. The best way to end a **dispute** is to
   a. shake hands.
   b. skip lunch.
   c. argue.
   d. wrestle.

Word Study • Context Clues 1

When you read, you may come across words that you do not know. When this happens, look for **context clues** in the sentence or surrounding sentences to help you figure out the word's meaning.

Read the sentences and explanations below to learn about three types of context clues.

Definition	*The house has an* **extensive** *yard, covering a large area.* The words *covering a large area* define *extensive*.
Example	*I like* **condiments** *such as ketchup, mustard, and relish on a burger.* The examples are "ketchup, mustard, and relish." This helps you understand that a condiment is something added to a food for flavor.
Restatement	*Very few plants grow well in* **arid**, *or dry, places.* The synonym *dry* explains the meaning of *arid*.

PRACTICE *Read each sentence. Write the meaning of the **boldface** word on the line. Then underline the words that helped you figure out its meaning.*

1. I was **elated**, totally thrilled, when I won the bike race. _____

2. The **pesky** mosquitoes were causing trouble and annoying our guests.

   _____

3. One day, I want to design **garments** such as dresses, suits, and skirts.

   _____

4. The lost hiker was **bewildered**, unsure about which of the two paths to take.

   _____

APPLY *Rewrite each sentence. Add context clues so that a reader can figure out the meaning of the **boldface** word in the sentence.*

5. I use different measuring **devices**.

   _____

6. The popular singer **shuns** photographers.

   _____

Speak *Make up a sentence using a unit word. The sentence should provide good context clues. Ask a partner to name the word and the clue to its meaning.*

Shades of Meaning • Adages and Proverbs 1

In the passage "Sybil Ludington's Ride" on pages 16–17, Sybil Ludington knew that her father was depending on her to make contact with the patriot volunteers. Sybil ran into several obstacles as she rode through the night, but she continued on until she accomplished her mission. Her success that night surely shows that she believed that **where there's a will, there's a way**.

A **proverb** or **adage** is a short, well-known expression or saying that states an obvious truth or gives advice. *Where there's a will, there's a way* is a proverb. It means that if you are determined to do something, you will figure out a way to make it happen.

PRACTICE *Read each sentence. Decide which proverb best expresses a truth about the situation described. Write the number of the sentence next to the proverb.*

1. Dad insisted we arrive at the store just as the doors open to take advantage of the sale.

2. No matter how many things the child had, he always thought his friends had more than he did.

3. I continued to look for my notebook long after my friends had stopped searching.

4. It always amazes me how much my sister is like my mother.

_4_ The apple doesn't fall far from the tree.

_1_ The early bird gets the worm.

_3_ Leave no stone unturned.

_2_ The grass is always greener on the other side of the street.

APPLY *Discuss each proverb with a partner. Then write a sentence to tell what the proverb means.*

5. Don't bite off more than you can chew.

   don't take more than you need

6. Nothing ventured, nothing gained.

   if you never take a risk you won't gain

7. Home is where the heart is.

   Home sweet home

8. Haste makes waste.

   if u rush you will mess up !!!

Introducing the Words

Read the following magazine article about a spectacular journey. Notice how the highlighted words are used. These are the words you will be learning in this unit.

Monarchs begin their long migration.

The Flight of the Monarch

(Magazine Article)

They are the only butterflies known to migrate, or travel, at a particular time of year. Some fly as far as 3,000 miles to reach their winter homes. They are also among the most vivid of all insects. Their bright orange, white, and black bodies can be seen flashing brilliantly in the sunlight. Their name is also appropriate because the monarch "rules" over the vast territory that it passes during its annual migration.

When the first cold winds of autumn blow, monarch butterflies in the United States begin their long migration south. They cannot postpone this flight, or their bodies might freeze. Monarchs in the eastern states migrate to warm havens in Mexico. For monarchs west of the Rocky Mountains, the winter destination is southern California.

Monarchs tend to migrate south in large groups, but weaker ones often straggle far behind. At night, the butterflies roost together in tall fir, cedar, and pine trees. Monarchs usually cover from fifty to one hundred miles a day, and it can take them up to two months to complete the trip.

The long flight south can be treacherous. Cold weather and early snowstorms often take a toll on the travelers. Monarchs must be cautious and try to avoid danger. Many birds feed on monarchs, too. Some butterflies run into obstacles, such as cars and trucks. Others just weaken and die from the strain of the difficult flight.

The bluffs and peaks of the Sierra Madre, a mountain range in Mexico, make an ideal

When its wings are open, the monarch is $3\frac{1}{2}$ to 4 inches wide.

High in the mountains of Mexico, monarchs wait out the winter.

haven for the monarchs. The fir forests there provide the right temperature and humidity. The butterflies gather in a few small areas in colonies that consist of millions and millions of individuals. A single tree might be home for more than ten thousand of the insects. The monarchs are not active at this time. Like bears, they sleep away the winter months.

To help preserve the monarchs, the Mexican government has taken steps to protect their winter home. For example, logging, or the cutting down of trees, is prohibited. Environmentalists despise this illegal activity, which shrinks the monarchs' habitat. Also, as the forest thins, the butterflies are more likely to get wet and freeze during winter rainstorms.

When the warm days of March arrive, the monarchs wake up and flutter down from their trees. After mating, the females lay their eggs. The eggs, which look like miniature pearls, hatch as caterpillars in about four days. After two weeks, each caterpillar transforms itself into a chrysalis, an egglike pod. Ten days later, the adult monarch emerges.

We must be clear when describing the migration of monarchs. The butterflies that flew south do not return north themselves. Only their offspring will begin the return flight in spring. Also, since most monarchs live only six weeks, it takes about three generations of monarchs to reach the northernmost states from Mexico. The females of each generation will deposit eggs along the route. Once grown, the new generation resumes the journey begun by its parents.

Fortunately, the generation of monarchs that is alive in early autumn lives much longer—about seven months. So those butterflies have time to make the long flight south. In this way, monarchs have populated large areas and lived on throughout the years.

Definitions

You were introduced to the words below in the passage on pages 26–27. Study the pronunciation, spelling, part of speech, and definition of each word. Write the word in the blank space in the sentence that follows. Then read the synonyms and antonyms.

1. bluff
(bluf)

(adj.) direct and outspoken in a good-natured way

He seemed a hearty, _____ fellow.

(n.) a steep, high cliff or bank; an attempt to fool someone

A scout stood on a _____ overlooking the valley.

(v.) to deceive or trick; to try to fool others by putting on a confident front

The thieves tried to _____ their way past the security guard.

SYNONYMS: (adj.) hearty; (n.) a ridge; a trick, hoax; (v.) to mislead, pretend, fake
ANTONYMS: (adj.) insincere, artful, sly

2. cautious
(kô′ shəs)

(adj.) avoiding unnecessary risks or mistakes

A _____ traveler prepares for emergencies.

SYNONYMS: careful, watchful, wary, guarded
ANTONYMS: daring, reckless, wild

3. consist
(kən sist′)

(v.) (used with of) to be made up of

Many salad dressings _____ of oil, vinegar, and spices.

SYNONYMS: to contain, include, involve, comprise

4. despise
(di spīz′)

(v.) to look down on intensely or feel contempt for, dislike strongly

I _____ bullies.

SYNONYMS: to hate, scorn, detest, loathe
ANTONYMS: to love, admire, esteem, adore, praise

5. haven
(hā′ vən)

(n.) a safe place

The captain sought a _____ from the storm.

SYNONYMS: a harbor, port, refuge, retreat, shelter, sanctuary
ANTONYMS: a trap, snare, ambush

6. miniature
(mi' nē ə chŭr)

(n.) a very small copy, model, or painting

Her collection of _____ is quite valuable.

(adj.) on a very small scale

A _____ railroad was on display in the toy department of the store.

SYNONYMS: (adj.) little, tiny, minute
ANTONYMS: (adj.) huge, giant

7. monarch
(mä' nərk)

(n.) a person who rules over a kingdom or empire

Queen Victoria was Great Britain's _____ from 1837 to 1901.

SYNONYMS: a ruler, king, queen, emperor, empress, czar
ANTONYMS: a subject, follower, commoner

8. obstacle
(äb' sti kəl)

(n.) something that gets in the way

Shyness need not be an _____ to success.

SYNONYMS: a hurdle, barrier, snag, hindrance
ANTONYMS: an aid, help, support, advantage

9. postpone
(pōst pōn')

(v.) to put off until later

Coach decided to _____ the practice.

SYNONYMS: to delay, suspend, shelve, defer
ANTONYMS: to advance, move up

10. straggle
(stra' gəl)

(v.) to stray off or trail behind; to spread out in a scattered fashion

Students who _____ from the group may get lost.

SYNONYMS: to ramble, drift, wander, roam, rove, detour

11. treacherous
(tre' chə rəs)

(adj.) likely to betray; seemingly safe but actually dangerous

That hill can be a _____ climb in winter.

SYNONYMS: disloyal, untrustworthy, unreliable; chancy, deceptive, tricky, hazardous
ANTONYMS: faithful, trustworthy; safe, harmless

12. vivid
(vi' vəd)

(adj.) bright and sharp, giving a clear picture; full of life

She gave a _____ description of her trip.

SYNONYMS: lively, intense, brilliant, dazzling, spirited, clear
ANTONYMS: lifeless, dull, drab, hazy, foggy

Match the Meaning

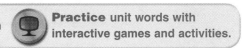
vocabularyworkshop.com

Practice unit words with interactive games and activities.

For each item below, choose the word whose meaning is suggested by the clue given. Then write the word in the space provided.

1. A picture so brilliant and bold that it seems alive might be called

_____.

   a. bluff   b. cautious   c. treacherous   d. vivid

2. A sundae _____ of ice cream and your choice of toppings.

   a. despises   b. consists   c. postpones   d. straggles

3. Something that blocks our way might be called a(n) _____.

   a. obstacle   b. bluff   c. haven   d. miniature

4. Hikers who stray from a trail or fall behind are guilty of

_____.

   a. consisting   b. despising   c. straggling   d. postponing

5. To try to fool others by acting very confident is to _____.

   a. consist   b. despise   c. straggle   d. bluff

6. If you _____ doing a chore, you will just have to do it later.

   a. bluff   b. postpone   c. straggle   d. despise

7. Walking on a decaying log that bridges a stream could be

_____.

   a. treacherous   b. cautious   c. miniature   d. bluff

8. To hate or to dislike something strongly is to _____ it.

   a. postpone   b. bluff   c. despise   d. consist

9. Another name for king is _____.

   a. haven   b. bluff   c. monarch   d. miniature

10. Boats seek a safe _____ where they can drop anchor for the night.

   a. bluff   b. obstacle   c. monarch   d. haven

11. A tiny copy of a full-sized object is known as a _____.

   a. bluff   b. miniature   c. haven   d. monarch

12. To avoid unnecessary risk is to act in a _____ way.

   a. cautious   b. vivid   c. miniature   d. treacherous

The rope-climb was the most difficult **obstacle** of the training course.

Synonyms

*For each item below, choose the word that is most nearly the **same** in meaning as the word or phrase in **boldface**. Then write your choice on the line provided.*

1. fake your way past the guard

   a. consist   b. despise   c. postpone   d. bluff   _____

2. wander from the route

   a. bluff   b. straggle   c. postpone   d. despise   _____

3. a peaceful **refuge** in the war-torn city

   a. haven   b. miniature   c. monarch   d. bluff   _____

4. a mix that **contained** flour, sugar, and baking powder

   a. bluffed   b. consisted of   c. despised   d. postponed   _____

5. a **watchful** driver

   a. miniature   b. treacherous   c. cautious   d. vivid   _____

6. a noble, wise, and generous **ruler**

   a. monarch   b. haven   c. obstacle   d. miniature   _____

Antonyms

*For each item below, choose the word that is most nearly **opposite** in meaning to the word or phrase in **boldface**. Then write your choice on the line provided.*

1. adore that kind of music

   a. consist   b. bluff   c. despise   d. straggle   _____

2. formed a **hazy** image

   a. treacherous   b. vivid   c. cautious   d. miniature   _____

3. to **move up** the ceremony one month

   a. postpone   b. bluff   c. despise   d. straggle   _____

4. a **huge** model of the castle

   a. cautious   b. treacherous   c. bluff   d. miniature   _____

5. a **faithful** servant

   a. treacherous   b. cautious   c. miniature   d. vivid   _____

6. no **advantage** to winning the election

   a. haven   b. obstacle   c. miniature   d. monarch   _____

Completing the Sentence

Choose the word from the box that best completes each item below. Then write the word in the space provided. (You may have to change the word's ending.)

bluff	cautious	consist
despise	haven	miniature
monarch	obstacle	postpone
straggle	treacherous	vivid

Americans Fight for Their Independence

■ King George III was the English _____ when American colonists began to grow impatient with English rule.

■ Even colonists who were eager for independence were _____ at first because they did not want a war.

■ But not all colonists _____ British rule; nearly one-third of them believed they should stay loyal to the King.

■ The first fight took place between 700 British soldiers and a small army that _____ of 70 American volunteers called Minutemen. The site of the battle was Lexington, Massachusetts.

■ In 1780, the American General Benedict Arnold took part in a _____ plot that nearly cost the lives of three thousand American soldiers.

■ After overcoming many _____, the Americans defeated the British, and King George recognized the United States as an independent nation.

A View from High Above

■ As we looked down from the rocky _____, we could see a small herd of wild ponies trotting in a field far below us.

■ We were so high above them that they looked like _____ horses.

■ One gray mare _____ behind the rest of the herd to protect her young foal.

A Getaway for Presidents

■ Since 1942, American presidents have used a quiet cabin retreat in Maryland as a _____ from the summer heat of Washington, D.C.

■ My Uncle David has _____ memories of the occasion when President Eisenhower renamed the retreat Camp David to honor the President's grandson.

■ A crisis might cause the President to _____ a planned visit to Camp David until the situation is under control.

Word Study • Homographs

Some multiple-meaning words are homographs. A **homograph** is a word with the same spelling as another word but with a different meaning and word origin. Sometimes the two words also have different pronunciations. For these reasons, homographs have separate entries in a dictionary. The word *bluff* (page 28) is a homograph. A **bluff** is a steep, high cliff or bank. *Bluff* also means "to deceive or trick."

Look at the chart for other examples of homographs. The small number after each **boldface** word indicates that the word has a separate dictionary entry.

racket[1]	(*n.*) a type of sports equipment that has a frame with strings and a handle
racket[2]	(*n.*) a loud disturbing noise
shore[1]	(*n.*) land along the edge of bodies of water
shore[2]	(*v.*) to prop up or support
desert[1]	(*n.*) a dry, barren area of land with little vegetation (**dez'** ûrt)
desert[2]	(*v.*) to leave or abandon (di **zûrt'**)

PRACTICE *Write the word from the chart that completes each sentence. Then write the number of the homograph whose meaning is illustrated.*

_____ **1.** From my window, I could hear the _____ made by the truck traffic.

_____ **2.** Cactus plants need little water and can grow well in the _____.

_____ **3.** We used wooden beams to _____ up the sagging old fence.

_____ **4.** People are often forced to _____ their homes during a flood.

_____ **5.** The professional tennis player has a custom-made _____.

_____ **6.** I like to walk along the _____ and look for shells.

APPLY *Complete each sentence using words from the chart above.*

7. I would drop my tennis _____ and quickly _____ the tennis court if a swarm of bees flew near me.

8. Down at the _____, the _____ of the seagulls' calls awakened me from my nap.

9. In the _____, the film crew had to _____ up the tent after the sudden sandstorm.

Write *Write a sentence that includes a pair of homographs.*

Example: I went *down* to the basement to get my warm *down* coat out of storage.

Vocabulary for Comprehension

*Read the following passage in which some of the words you have studied in Units 1–3 appear in **boldface**. Then answer the questions on page 35.*

The Tallest Sailor in the World

Long ago, a thunderous wave crashed on the shores of Cape Cod. Moments later, a loud cry split the air. The worried villagers rushed to the **bluff** overlooking the beach. They were shocked to find that the noise had come from a **solitary** baby—a baby who was 6 feet tall! The locals put the giant baby in a cart and hauled him into town. They named him Alfred Bulltop Stormalong, but called him Stormy.

Stormy grew to love the sea. He loved swimming in the deep, even **treacherous**, water, and he rode sea monsters for fun. He was fearless. Once, he even turned an old house upside down and tried to sail away in it.

Stormy grew to be 36 feet tall, and Cape Cod became too small for him. **Abandoning** Cape Cod, Stormy traveled to Boston. There

he became the captain of a mighty large ship called *The Courser*. Stormy was no ordinary captain. He ate stew from a rowboat, and he slept in the mainsail.

Stormalong's sailing skills were **impressive**, too. In one adventure, Stormy was sailing his ship through the English Channel when he discovered that the waterway was barely wider than the ship. Expecting a tight fit, Stormy told the crew to soap the sides of the ship. Although it slipped through, the huge ship scraped the Dover cliffs, leaving behind a thick layer of soap. These cliffs have been pure white ever since. While some may say Stormy is just a **myth**, folks at Dover say the Channel is still foamy from the soap.

Fill in the circle next to the choice that best completes the sentence or answers the question.

1. In this passage, the meaning of **bluff** is
   (a) to deceive or trick.
   (b) a steep, high cliff.
   (c) a large wave.
   (d) a loud sound.

2. The meaning of **solitary** is
   (a) friendly.
   (b) temporary.
   (c) just one.
   (d) tiny.

3. Alfred Bulltop Stormalong spent most of his time
   (a) in Boston.
   (b) near or at sea.
   (c) far inland.
   (d) on Cape Cod.

4. Another word for **treacherous** is
   (a) tiring.
   (b) calm.
   (c) dangerous.
   (d) cautious.

5. In this passage, the meaning of **abandoning** is
   (a) visiting.
   (b) forsaking.
   (c) occupying.
   (d) crossing.

6. **Impressive** most nearly means
   (a) commanding attention.
   (b) fading away.
   (c) plentiful.
   (d) continuous.

7. In this passage, the meaning of **myth** is
   (a) something imaginary.
   (b) something from history.
   (c) a scientific explanation.
   (d) a terrible mistake.

8. The author most likely wrote this passage to
   (a) give facts about a real person.
   (b) persuade people to become sailors.
   (c) give facts about life on a ship.
   (d) entertain readers with a story.

Write Your Own

Think about other American myths and legends that you know. On a separate sheet of paper, write to retell a story about another famous character. Use at least three words from Units 1–3.

Introducing the Words

Read the following diary entries about a girl's journey west during the time of the California Gold Rush. Notice how the highlighted words are used. These are the words you will be learning in this unit.

Wagon Train Diary
(Diary Entries)

May 1, **1849**   Today, we said good-bye and started off to the land of gold. There are thirty wagons in our group and sixty people. We began with much laughter, but a mishap quickly spoiled the mood. While crossing the Missouri River, two wagons were swept away by the water, and the families inside barely escaped.

May 15   The oxen plod on, slowly and steadily. How I wish they moved at a more aggressive pace! When it rains, we barely cover two miles in a day. Will we ever reach California? Everyone who emigrates wonders this, for the hours drag slowly. The bumping wagon bruises my bones, so usually I walk. My feet are sore, but the prairie flowers are beautiful, and I would not see them so well from the wagon.

May 18   Just before noon, the sky looked hazy. I thought it must be full of smoke, but then we heard the buzzing and knew it was a swarm of grasshoppers in flight. There were more of them than anyone could imagine. The giant cloud of grasshoppers overwhelmed us,

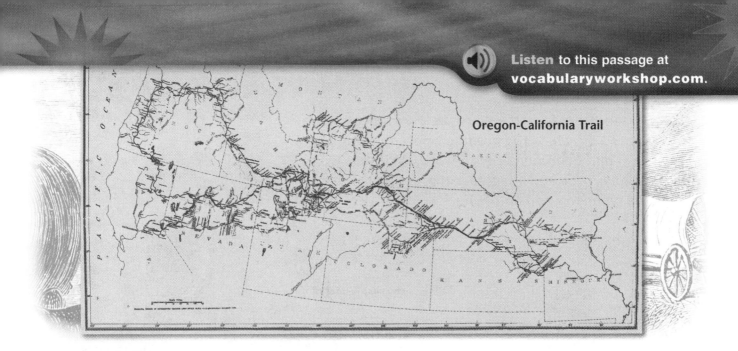

Oregon-California Trail

turning day to night. We did all we could to keep the pests off our faces until, mercifully, they moved on.

June 3 Hurrah! Today, we reached the Platte River. After weeks of dusty travel, how luxurious to sit in the water. The taste of fish is indeed a welcome change after salted pork. If only we could linger here, but we dare not. The wide span of a desert and the tall masses of a mountain range await us.

June 19 At Independence Rock, so many emigrants have cut their names into the granite that I could barely find a spot for my own. Now

my name will forever be associated with this landmark on the trail leading west.

July 6 We took a cutoff and got lost. At last, we are heading the right way, but the oxen need water. Once we thought we saw a stream, but it was a mirage—a trick of sunlight that deceived us.

August 6 It seemed like there would be no end to the wind and dust. Seven of our wagons turned back. Then there was a sight to behold at Soda Springs. Hot water puffed and spurted high into the air, leaving a trail of rainbows. I wouldn't have traded that beauty for the glamour of any big city.

August 20 Grass is scarce, and the oxen groan. We had to lighten our load, and Father dumped our stove and pots and books. Necessity has made us flexible, and we cannot be too attached to our belongings. The long trail is littered with lovely things.

September 8 Today, we traveled fourteen miles and had to cross the Truckee River twelve times.

September 15 Never did we believe that we'd make it up the rocky trail to the top of the Sierra Nevada, a mountain range in California, but here we are, and the majestic pines and peaks frame our first grand glimpse of California!

Definitions

You were introduced to the words below in the passage on pages 36–37. Study the pronunciation, spelling, part of speech, and definition of each word. Write the word in the blank space in the sentence that follows. Then read the synonyms and antonyms.

1. aggressive
(ə gre' siv)

(adj.) quick to fight or quarrel, tending to violence; bold and forceful, determined

An _____ salesperson never gives up.

SYNONYMS: violent, warlike; pushy, vigorous
ANTONYMS: peaceful, timid; shy, bashful, retiring

2. associate
(v., ə sō' shē āt;
n., adj., ə sō' shē ət)

(v.) to join or be together as partners, allies, or friends; to link in one's mind, connect

I will always _____ peaches with summer.

(n.) a partner, friend

The businessman introduced his _____.

(adj.) having less than full rank

She was hired as an _____ professor in the science department.

SYNONYMS: (v.) to unite, mingle, combine, mix, relate; (n.) a companion, teammate, coworker; (adj.) assistant
ANTONYMS: (v.) to separate, distance, divorce; (n.) an enemy, foe, rival, stranger

3. deceive
(di sēv')

(v.) to trick or lead a person into believing something that is not true

It is wrong to _____ the customer with false advertising.

SYNONYMS: to fool, swindle, mislead, double-cross, cheat

4. emigrate
(e' mə grāt)

(v.) to leave one's home country or area to live in another

Henri hopes to _____ from Haiti to the United States.

SYNONYMS: to relocate, resettle, move, migrate

5. flexible
(flek' sə bəl)

(adj.) able to bend without breaking; able to change or to take in new ideas

I brought in a box of _____ straws.

SYNONYMS: bendable, limber, elastic, springy; adaptable, adjustable
ANTONYMS: stiff, rigid, unbendable; inflexible

6. glamour
(gla′ mər)

(n.) mysterious charm, beauty, or attractiveness

The movie captures the _____ of Paris.

SYNONYMS: style, sparkle, magic, enchantment, romance, fascination

7. hazy
(hā′ zē)

(adj.) unclear, misty; not readily seen or understandable

Another hot and _____ day is forecast.

SYNONYMS: cloudy, smoggy, foggy, blurry, dim; vague
ANTONYMS: bright, clear; precise

8. linger
(liŋ′ gər)

(v.) to stay longer than expected, be slow in leaving; to go slowly or take one's time

We like to _____ over breakfast on Saturdays.

SYNONYMS: to delay, stall, remain, stay, lag, persist; to dawdle
ANTONYMS: to hurry, rush, charge, hasten

9. luxurious
(ləg zhůr′ ē əs)

(adj.) providing ease and comfort far beyond what is ordinary or necessary

They took a _____ vacation.

SYNONYMS: rich, elegant, pleasurable, lavish, extravagant, fancy
ANTONYMS: poor, plain, simple, modest

10. mishap
(mis′ hap)

(n.) an unfortunate but minor accident

The waiters chuckled over the _____.

SYNONYMS: a misfortune, mistake, blunder, slipup

11. overwhelm
(ō vər welm′)

(v.) to overcome by superior force, crush; to affect so deeply as to make helpless

Fresh troops threatened to _____ the weakened defenders.

SYNONYMS: to overpower, destroy, crush; to stun, shock, stagger, astound

12. span
(span)

(n.) the full reach or length, especially between two points in space or time

The _____ of most insects' lives is very brief.

(v.) to stretch or reach across

A new bridge will be built to _____ the Golden Gate, which is the opening of San Francisco Bay.

SYNONYMS: (n.) extent, distance, length, scope, period; (v.) to bridge, cross, last

Match the Meaning

vocabularyworkshop.com 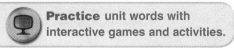 **Practice** unit words with interactive games and activities.

For each item below, choose the word whose meaning is suggested by the clue given. Then write the word in the space provided.

1. People who are too _____ often get into quarrels or fights.
   a. flexible   b. hazy   c. luxurious   d. aggressive

2. To fool people into believing what is not true is to _____ them.
   a. overwhelm   b. deceive   c. emigrate   d. linger

3. If you join with me as a partner, you _____ with me.
   a. associate   b. deceive   c. overwhelm   d. span

4. It is not easy to see distant mountains on a(n) _____ day.
   a. aggressive   b. flexible   c. hazy   d. luxurious

5. A princess's charm and beauty might make her a symbol of

   _____.

   a. associate   b. mishap   c. span   d. glamour

6. To _____ from Korea to Nepal is to leave Korea to live in Nepal.
   a. associate   b. emigrate   c. linger   d. overwhelm

7. Getting a paper cut is an example of a minor _____.
   a. mishap   b. span   c. associate   d. glamour

8. A mighty army might easily _____ a weaker foe.
   a. emigrate   b. linger   c. overwhelm   d. associate

9. A(n) _____ straw makes it easy to drink from a juice box.
   a. luxurious   b. aggressive   c. flexible   d. hazy

10. A _____ hotel might provide six fluffy bath towels for each guest.
   a. aggressive   b. hazy   c. flexible   d. luxurious

11. To stay longer than expected or to leave slowly is to _____.
   a. deceive   b. linger   c. emigrate   d. span

12. A bridge that crosses the Mississippi is said to _____ that river.
   a. span   b. associate   c. linger   d. overwhelm

The family quickly cleaned up the mishap before the paint dried.

Synonyms

*For each item below, choose the word that is most nearly the **same** in meaning as the word or phrase in **boldface**. Then write your choice on the line provided.*

1. the **magic** of Hollywood

a. mishap   b. span   c. glamour   d. associate   _____

2. crush our opponents

a. deceive   b. emigrate   c. linger   d. overwhelm   _____

3. told us about the **slipup**

a. glamour   b. span   c. mishap   d. associate   _____

4. move from Egypt to Italy

a. overwhelm   b. linger   c. deceive   d. emigrate   _____

5. mislead the enemy

a. associate   b. deceive   c. overwhelm   d. emigrate   _____

6. over the **period** of a year

a. associate   b. mishap   c. span   d. glamour   _____

Antonyms

*For each item below, choose the word that is most nearly **opposite** in meaning to the word or phrase in **boldface**. Then write your choice on the line provided.*

1. timid base runners

a. associate   b. aggressive   c. luxurious   d. hazy   _____

2. introduced her **rival**

a. glamour   b. associate   c. span   d. mishap   _____

3. hurry over our good-byes

a. span   b. emigrate   c. overwhelm   d. linger   _____

4. a **rigid** point of view

a. flexible   b. aggressive   c. hazy   d. luxurious   _____

5. a **simple** meal with friends

a. aggressive   b. flexible   c. luxurious   d. hazy   _____

6. a **clear** sky

a. flexible   b. luxurious   c. aggressive   d. hazy   _____

Completing the Sentence

Choose the word from the box that best completes each item below. Then write the word in the space provided. (You may have to change the word's ending.)

A New Life in America

■ Poor conditions in their homeland have driven many Mexicans to

_____ to the United States. Many have settled in the Southwest, but others have traveled to big cities in the Midwest and Northeast in search of work.

■ Some dishonest agents _____ travelers by taking their money in exchange for legal documents that they never provide.

■ Over the _____ of the past fifty years, more immigrants have come to the United States from Mexico than from any other country.

■ Many immigrants have only a(n) _____ notion of what life will be like in the new country they have heard so much about.

■ Mix-ups over language or local customs often lead to _____ and misunderstandings.

■ Despite facing some _____ problems, most immigrants manage to build better lives for themselves and their families.

A Legal Brief

■ It is a lawyer's duty to act in a(n) _____ fashion in order to protect the interests of his or her clients. Trial lawyers especially cannot afford to be timid or shy.

■ Most lawyers, like other professionals, have to keep _____ hours in order to serve their clients well.

■ From the newest _____ to senior partners, lawyers must research past cases to find ways to support their arguments. For this reason, they often spend long hours in law libraries.

■ Media attention lends some legal cases more _____ than they really deserve. Some especially newsworthy trials are now televised from start to finish.

■ The impact of such cases may _____ in the public mind long after all the lawyers, the judge, and the jurors have left the courtroom.

■ Lawyers on television and in movies are often seen to drive _____ cars and wear expensive clothes. In fact, most real-life lawyers work long, hard hours and rarely enjoy the spotlight of celebrity.

Word Associations

*Circle the letter next to the word or expression that best completes the sentence or answers the question. Pay special attention to the word in **boldface**.*

1. Which is an example of a **mishap**?
   a. solving a riddle
   b. a serious car accident
   c. stepping in a puddle
   d. telling a lie

2. If a movie **overwhelms** you, you
   a. might feel like you will cry.
   b. might ask for a refund.
   c. might refuse to clap.
   d. might get very hungry.

3. If you have a **hazy** grasp of map reading, you should
   a. use a brighter lamp.
   b. memorize the state capitals.
   c. take the bus.
   d. learn more about keys and symbols.

4. You might **linger** if you are
   a. not wearing a watch.
   b. late for an appointment.
   c. having a great time.
   d. bored to tears.

5. A **luxurious** outfit might include
   a. gold jewelry.
   b. rags.
   c. T-shirts.
   d. aluminum foil.

6. Which would most people **associate**?
   a. bicycles with snowshoes
   b. winter with fireworks
   c. fishing with homework
   d. vacations with summer

7. In a place known for **glamour**, a visitor might find
   a. cows grazing in a field.
   b. unpaved roads.
   c. lots of factories.
   d. expensive restaurants.

8. **Aggressive** ballplayers would
   a. lose interest in the game.
   b. play as hard as they can.
   c. let their opponents win.
   d. ask to sit out the game.

9. You might **deceive** a puppy by
   a. pretending to throw a ball.
   b. taking off its collar.
   c. feeding it twice a day.
   d. changing your clothes.

10. A U.S. citizen might **emigrate** to
    a. the moon.
    b. Florida.
    c. Canada.
    d. New York City.

11. The "**span** of a lifetime" means
    a. from Monday to Friday.
    b. from birth to death.
    c. from kindergarten to college.
    d. from breakfast to dinner.

12. Which is the most **flexible**?
    a. a frying pan
    b. a pipe wrench
    c. an extension ladder
    d. a garden hose

Word Study • Analogies

An **analogy** is a statement that shows how two pairs of words are related. Here is an analogy with the word *flexible* (page 38): *twig* is to *flexible* as *cotton* is to *soft*.

In this analogy, the first word in each pair names an object, and the second word gives a description of the object. *Twig* can be described as *flexible*, and *cotton* can be described as *soft*.

The chart at the right shows other types of relationships that analogies can have.

Object/ Description	*twig* is to *flexible* as *cotton* is to *soft*
Synonyms	*vivid* is to *bright* as *dull* is to *boring*
Antonyms	*left* is to *right* as *even* is to *odd*
Object/Class	*rose* is to *flower* as *pine* is to *tree*
Object/Function	*fork* is to *eat* as *pencil* is to *write*

PRACTICE *Match the word pairs to form a complete analogy. Write the number of the first pair next to the pair with the same relationship.*

1. *keyboard* is to *type* as   _____ *trout* is to *fish*

2. *lemon* is to *sour* as   _____ *luxurious* is to *plain*

3. *linger* is to *rush* as   _____ *scissors* is to *cut*

4. *robin* is to *bird* as   _____ *honey* is to *sweet*

APPLY *Complete each analogy. Explain the relationship on the lines provided.*

5. *strawberry* is to *fruit* as *carrot* is to _____

_____

6. *ruler* is to *measure* as *microscope* is to _____

_____

7. *cheetah* is to *fast* as *snail* is to _____

_____

8. *fearless* is to *timid* as *hazy* is to _____

_____

9. *justify* is to *defend* as *deceive* is to _____

_____

 Speak *Create an analogy using a word from Units 1–4. Have a partner complete the analogy. Talk about the relationship between the words.*

Shades of Meaning • Words That Describe Behavior

In the passage "Wagon Train Diary" on pages 36–37, you read: *How I wish they moved at a more **aggressive** pace!* Here, *aggressive* describes the way the narrator would like the oxen to move. She wishes that they would move with more energy.

Aggressive can also be used to describe behavior, the way in which a person or animal acts. Look at the words in the chart. Each describes a particular behavior.

aggressive	A person who is **aggressive** is quick to attack or start a fight.
arrogant	A person who is **arrogant** feels very proud, believing that others are much less important.
assertive	A person who is **assertive** stands up for himself or herself and tells others what he or she thinks or wants.
impulsive	A person who is **impulsive** acts without thinking carefully first.

PRACTICE *Write the word from the chart that best describes each behavior.*

1. She jumped right into the pool without taking her shoes off. _____

2. The dog growled and bared its teeth when we walked by. _____

3. He always thinks his ideas are the best in the class. _____

4. She won the student council election because she is not afraid to speak her mind.

_____

5. The athlete defended his request for practice time on the basketball court.

_____

6. At the auction, the woman bid on an item she didn't even want. _____

7. Because he believed he had the best plan, the candidate thought everyone would vote

for him. _____

APPLY *Give an example of when you have shown or seen each of the behaviors below.*

8. aggressive _____

9. arrogant _____

10. assertive _____

11. impulsive _____

Introducing the Words

Read the following ancient myth about what happens after a poor couple meets a pair of travelers. Notice how the highlighted words are used. These are the words you will be learning in this unit.

Baucis and Philemon

(Ancient Myth)

In his palace on Mount Olympus, Jupiter, the supreme Roman god, was furious. "People are so corrupt!" he told his grandson Mercury. "They lie, they cheat, they steal—it's a disgrace."

"Is it really that bad?" asked Mercury.

"Worse," replied Jupiter. "People don't even show hospitality to strangers anymore." This last blemish on the character of humans bothered Jupiter the most. Welcoming guests kindly was important to the king of the gods. "I have to teach people a lesson!" the great god continued.

"Before you unjustly accuse people and persecute them, let's travel to Earth and see for ourselves," suggested Mercury. "Maybe there are more good people than you think."

Using Mercury's winged sandals, the two gods transported themselves to the city of Phrygia. There, they disguised themselves in ragged cloaks so that no one would know they were gods. Looking at them, you would conclude that they were poor travelers.

From house to house, the two nomads wandered, asking for water and bread. Sad to say, the situation was as bad as Jupiter had predicted. No one welcomed the travelers.

"On your way!" one farmer warned, threatening to turn his dogs loose on them.

"Get out of here!" a woman shouted, waving a blunt ax.

So it went at every house in the city until at last the travelers came to Baucis and Philemon. Their one-room hut was falling down, for Baucis and Philemon were poor. They were also old, in their eighties, and had been married sixty years.

"Come in, come in!" Philemon welcomed the strangers. "You have walked a long way, for I can see the dust and the fatigue on your faces."

"Will you stay for dinner?" Philemon's wife Baucis asked. "It isn't much—fruit, bread and olives—but you're welcome to share our meal with us."

The gods sat down at the rough wooden table, and Baucis lit candles to give the meal a festive atmosphere. As Philemon served the food, Baucis again apologized for the meal. "We live very simply," she said. "The important thing is that we love each other."

Philemon nodded, but he had just detected something very strange. He brought his guests more food and drink every time their plates were empty, yet the serving pot and jug remained full. Only a god was capable of such a miracle!

Reading Philemon's mind, Jupiter and Mercury threw off their cloaks and shone in all their glory. "In this entire city," Jupiter said, "only this house has shown us hospitality."

As he spoke, another wonder occurred. The wooden hut fell away and in its place stood a shining marble house. "Tell me what you wish for most," said Jupiter, "and I will give it to you."

"Let this building be your temple, and let us be the priests here," Philemon began.

"And let us die together, so neither ever has to live without the other," Baucis concluded.

And so it was. Baucis and Philemon served in the temple for many years, and when they were about to die, Jupiter turned them into trees—an oak and a linden. Remarkably, both trees grew from the same trunk. Together, their long branches shaded the temple for generations.

Definitions

You were introduced to the words below in the passage on pages 46–47. Study the pronunciation, spelling, part of speech, and definition of each word. Write the word in the blank space in the sentence that follows. Then read the synonyms and antonyms.

1. **blemish**
   (ble′ mish)

   (n.) a mark or stain that damages the appearance of something; a weakness or flaw

   The carpenter noticed a _blemish_ in the finish of the cabinet.

   SYNONYMS: a scar, spot, smudge; a defect, weak spot

2. **blunt**
   (blunt)

   (adj.) having a dull point or edge, not sharp; honest but insensitive in manner

   My uncle gave me some _blunt_ advice.

   (v.) to make less sharp

   Misuse will _blunt_ a knife blade.

   SYNONYMS: (adj.) dull; outspoken, frank, direct
   ANTONYMS: (adj.) sharp, keen; tactful, diplomatic; (v.) to sharpen

3. **capable**
   (kā′ pə bəl)

   (adj.) able and prepared to do something; fit or skilled

   A _capable_ teacher should be rewarded.

   SYNONYM: qualified
   ANTONYMS: unqualified, incapable, unfit

4. **conclude**
   (kən klüd′)

   (v.) to finish; to bring something to an end; to decide after careful thought

   After electing a new secretary, the committee voted to _conclude_ the meeting.

   SYNONYMS: to close, complete, stop; to reason, judge
   ANTONYMS: to open, begin, start, commence

5. **detect**
   (di tekt′)

   (v.) to find or discover something, notice

   A test may _detect_ chemicals in the water supply.

   SYNONYMS: to observe, spot
   ANTONYMS: to miss, overlook

6. fatigue
(fə tēg′)

(n.) weariness or exhaustion from work or lack of sleep

By the end of the day, I felt overcome with ___*fatigue*___.

(v.) to make very tired

The riders were warned not to ___*fatigue*___ *the horses.*

SYNONYMS: (n.) tiredness, sleepiness, weakness; (v.) to tire
ANTONYMS: (n.) liveliness, energy; (v.) to energize, perk up

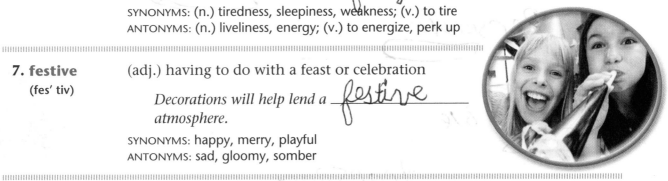

7. festive
(fes′ tiv)

(adj.) having to do with a feast or celebration

Decorations will help lend a ___*festive*___ *atmosphere.*

SYNONYMS: happy, merry, playful
ANTONYMS: sad, gloomy, somber

8. hospitality
(häs pə ta′ lə tē)

(n.) a friendly welcome and treatment of guests

The innkeepers were famous for their ___*hospitality*___

SYNONYMS: friendliness, generosity, warmth
ANTONYMS: unfriendliness, hostility

9. nomad
(nō′ mad)

(n.) a member of a people who move from place to place; a person who roams aimlessly

The adventurer lived the life of a ___*nomad*___.

SYNONYMS: a wanderer, roamer, rover

10. persecute
(pûr′ si kyüt)

(v.) to treat unjustly or cause to suffer

The dictator may try to ___*persecute*___ *the minority group.*

SYNONYMS: to torment, hurt, annoy
ANTONYMS: to reward, favor, comfort, help, protect

11. supreme
(sə prēm′)

(adj.) highest in power, rank, authority, quality, or degree

He acted as if giving up his seat were the ___*supreme*___ *sacrifice.*

SYNONYMS: first, greatest, dominant, outstanding
ANTONYMS: low, lowly, worst

12. transport
(v., trans pôrt′;
n., trans′ pôrt)

(v.) to move or carry from one place to another

A mover was hired to ___*transport*___ *the furniture.*

(n.) a vehicle used to move things from place to place;
the act or process of moving something from one place to another

The ocean liner was used as a troop ___*transport*___ *during the war.*

SYNONYMS: (v.) to haul, cart, send, convey

Match the Meaning

vocabularyworkshop.com

Practice unit words with interactive games and activities.

For each item below, choose the word whose meaning is suggested by the clue given. Then write the word in the space provided.

1. People who never settle down in one place are called __nomads__
   a. blemishes   b. transports   c. hospitalities   d. nomads

2. To __Persecute__ someone is to be cruel to that person.
   a. conclude   b. persecute   c. blunt   d. detect

3. To prove your ability at something is to show yourself
   __Capable__
   a. capable   b. festive   c. supreme   d. blunt

4. A train is a good form of __transport__ if you want to enjoy the scenery.
   a. nomad   b. transport   c. blemish   d. fatigue

5. Weddings and birthdays are examples of __festive__ events.
   a. blunt   b. capable   c. festive   d. supreme

6. To notice something is to __detect__ it.
   a. detect   b. conclude   c. persecute   d. blunt

7. You can usually overcome __hospitality__ by getting a good night's sleep.
   fatigue
   a. transport   b. blemishes   c. fatigue   d. hospitality

8. The __Supreme__ Court is the highest in the land.
   a. Supreme   b. Blunt   c. Festive   d. Capable

9. It's a good idea to __Conclude__ a speech with a summary.
   a. blunt   b. conclude   c. detect   d. persecute

10. A smudge in a paint job is an example of a __blemish__.
   a. blemish   b. transport   c. nomad   d. hospitality

11. Improper use of a knife may __blunt__ its edge.
   a. detect   b. transport   c. blunt   d. conclude

12. Good hosts would be sure to show __hospitality__
   a. transport   b. hospitality   c. blemish   d. fatigue

An experienced jeweler will likely spot every **blemish** in a gemstone.

Synonyms

For each item below, choose the word that is most nearly the **same** in meaning as the word or phrase in **boldface**. Then write your choice on the line provided.

1. her **outstanding** accomplishment
   a. blunt   b. festive   (c. supreme)   d. capable   *Supreme*

2. tried to conceal the **flaw**
   (a. blemish)   b. nomad   ~~c. fatigue~~   d. hospitality   *fatigue* *blemish*

3. **carry** the grain to distant markets
   a. conclude   b. detect   c. blunt   (d. transport)   *transport*

4. a **skilled** performer, but not a star
   a. supreme   (b. capable)   c. blunt   d. festive   *capable*

5. followed the trail of **wanderers**
   a. transports   b. blemishes   c. nomads   d. hospitalities   _____

6. a **happy** atmosphere
   (a. festive)   b. capable   c. supreme   d. blunt   *festive*

Antonyms

For each item below, choose the word that is most nearly **opposite** in meaning to the word or phrase in **boldface**. Then write your choice on the line provided.

1. **overlook** the danger
   (a. detect)   b. conclude   c. persecute   d. transport   *detect*

2. spoke in a **diplomatic** manner
   a. supreme   (b. festive)   c. blunt   d. capable   *festive*

3. **begin** the homework project
   a. detect   b. persecute   c. transport   (d. conclude)   *conclude*

4. **protected** the strangers
   a. blunted   (b. persecuted)   c. concluded   d. detected   *pers*

5. surprised by their **liveliness**
   a. nomad   b. blemish   c. fatigue   d. hospitality   *fati*

6. showed **unfriendliness** to the visitors
   a. fatigue   (b. hospitality)   c. transports   d. blemishes   _____

Completing the Sentence

Choose the word from the box that best completes each item below. Then write the word in the space provided. (You may have to change the word's ending.)

blemish	blunt	capable
conclude	detect	fatigue
festive	hospitality	nomad
persecute	supreme	transport

Speaking Out Against Bias

■ The principal did not mince her words but spoke in _blunt_ terms on the subject of prejudice to the students assembled in the school auditorium.

■ She described the ugly insult that had been written on a wall as a _persecute_ on the school's honor.

■ She went on to warn that she would not allow a handful of students to be _persecute_ just because they held different religious beliefs from most.

■ "Sometimes it requires a _supreme_ effort," she said, "to overcome our prejudices and respect the dignity of others."

■ She asked that everyone work together to make ours a school that is known for the _hospitality_ it shows to all.

On the Move

■ Though many Native American peoples lived in settled villages and farmed the land, many others lived the life of _nomads_.

■ The nomadic tribes of the Great Plains marked successful buffalo hunts with _festive_ ceremonies of thanks.

■ In Asia the nomadic Kazakhs use camels to _transport_ their tents, called *yurts*, and other belongings from place to place.

■ Because they lose body water very slowly, camels are _capable_ of traveling for days, even in extreme heat, without drinking a drop.

A Train Derails

■ The safety panel looking into the train crash _fatig_ that the most likely cause was human error.

■ It was learned that the engineer had not slept in over 36 hours and was probably suffering from extreme _blemish_.

■ Furthermore, tests of the equipment did not _____ any signs of failure in the train's braking system.

Word Associations

*Circle the letter next to the word or expression that best completes the sentence or answers the question. Pay special attention to the word in **boldface**.*

1. If you feel **fatigue**, you might
a. take a nap.
b. run 3 miles.
c. swim 50 laps.
d. clean out the garage.

2. Which cannot offer **hospitality**?
a. a school
b. a gift box
c. a town
d. a person

3. Someone who is **blunt** might
a. cheer you up.
b. hurt your feelings.
c. lie to you.
d. forget your birthday.

4. Which is a **festive** event?
a. a final exam
b. a terrible tragedy
c. a birthday party
d. a criminal trial

5. A **capable** student is one who
a. travels a long way to school.
b. misses a lot of school.
c. does well in school.
d. knows everyone in school.

6. Which of the following might you use to **detect** something?
a. a pencil
b. a magnifying glass
c. a sandwich
d. a pair of scissors

7. A **blemished** jewel will probably
a. cost less than a flawless one.
b. be stolen.
c. be found in a museum.
d. cost more than a flawless one.

8. A good detective might **conclude** a robbery case by
a. turning in her badge.
b. looking for clues.
c. having donuts and coffee.
d. arresting the thief.

9. Your **supreme** achievement is
a. your greatest.
b. your worst.
c. your first.
d. your last.

10. A **nomad's** home might be
a. an apartment.
b. a castle.
c. a tent.
d. a farmhouse.

11. If I were **persecuted**, I would
a. feel happy.
b. feel hungry.
c. feel hurt.
d. feel sleepy.

12. Which might **transport** an elephant?
a. a skateboard
b. a shopping cart
c. a hot-air balloon
d. a big truck

Word Study • Words Often Confused

Words that look similar and have similar pronunciations but that have different meanings often cause confusion. For example, the word *persecute* (page 49) is often confused with the word *prosecute*. Read this sentence: *The king who had* **persecuted** *the peasants was* **prosecuted** *for his crimes.* Here, *persecuted* means "caused to suffer" and *prosecuted* means "to bring legal action against."

Look at the chart to find other examples of words that are often confused.

access	(*n.*) an entrance or approach
excess	(*adj.*) beyond what is needed; extra
advice	(*n.*) an idea that is offered
advise	(*v.*) to give help and information
cease	(*v.*) to stop
seize	(*v.*) to take hold of

PRACTICE *Underline the word in* **boldface** *that best completes the sentence.*

1. During a trip to the restaurant, our class was given (**access**, **excess**) to the kitchen.

2. At closing time each day, the workers store (**access**, **excess**) food in large refrigerators.

3. When I could not decide which club to join, I asked my friend for (**advise**, **advice**).

4. "Please (**advise**, **advice**) me on what to do," I said.

5. The wind blew so hard I had to (**cease**, **seize**) the rail to keep from falling.

6. The windstorm did not (**cease**, **seize**) for the rest of the day.

APPLY *Complete each sentence using a* **boldface** *word from the chart above.*

7. I ___advise___ you to ___seize___ my arm if you feel as if you might fall.

8. Before we gain ___access___ to the beach, we must wait for the storms to ___cease___.

9. The business owner hired an accountant to give her _____ about

   spending the _____ funds.

Write *Here are two more word pairs that can cause confusion. Write a sentence for each of the words. Then look in a dictionary to make sure you used each word correctly.*

picture / pitcher   **costume / custom**

I saw a picture of the pitcher in a magazine

Shades of Meaning • Words That Name Travelers

In the passage "Baucis and Philemon" on pages 46–47, you read this sentence: *From house to house, the two **nomads** wandered, asking for water and bread.* In the passage, Jupiter and Mercury are the *nomads*. They are travelers wandering the city of Phrygia and looking for someone to show them hospitality.

Here are some other words that name travelers. Notice that one difference among the travelers is their purpose for traveling.

nomad	A **nomad** roams from place to place.
commuter	A **commuter** travels a long distance between home and work.
tourist	A **tourist** travels to visit a place for pleasure.
pilgrim	A **pilgrim** journeys to a sacred place, usually for religious reasons.

PRACTICE *Write the word from the chart that best names the person making each statement.*

1. I traveled a great distance to visit a holy shrine. _Pilgrim_
2. I take the train to work every day. _Commuter_
3. I never live in one place for a long time. _nomad_
4. I went to the Grand Canyon to see the sights. _tourist_
5. Each year, I travel with my family to visit the origins of my religion. _Pilgrim_
6. The job requires me to be in Boston every month. _Commuter_

APPLY *Answer each question to show the meaning of the word in boldface. Be sure to use the boldfaced word in your answer.*

7. Who is a **commuter** you know? Why is that person a commuter?
   My Mom was a commuter She went to boston everyday.

8. What might a **tourist** do in your area?
   A tourist might come to see the seasons.

9. What are some examples of places a **pilgrim** might travel to?
   A pilgrim might travel to the Kathedral

10. What reasons might a person have for being a **nomad**?
   A nomad might not like were he lives

Introducing the Words

Read the following biography about a famous American poet. Notice how the highlighted words are used. These are the words you will be learning in this unit.

The Surprising Life of Emily Dickinson

(Biography)

Once upon a time, in the town of Amherst, Massachusetts, lived a young girl named Emily Dickinson. She was a lively, happy child who lived with her parents, sister, and brother in a big house near the village green. At school, Emily learned to read and write, and at home, she learned to cook and sew. Like many of her friends, she no doubt had a great capacity for fun as well, sledding in the cold New England winter and going on picnics in the green and flowering summertime.

There was nothing unusual about young Emily. It seemed apparent that she would get married one day. Eventually, she would have her own house and raise her own children, perhaps in Amherst. In many ways, she would duplicate the life that her mother had lived. After all, that's what most girls did in the 1800s.

When she was older, Emily went away to college for a while. She took a few trips, too, once traveling to Washington, D.C., where her father was a congressman. At home, she took part in town and church activities. When the Civil War began, she worked with other civilians to find ways to support the soldiers.

Then, suddenly, everything changed. For some reason, Emily decided to withdraw from everyday life. She stopped seeing almost everyone, never traveled, and rarely went outside. Eventually, she didn't leave her parents' house at all, and that's how she lived for the rest of her life.

What provoked Emily Dickinson to take this course of action? Even today, no one can say for sure. While the undoing of her normal social life must have caused loneliness and pain, it also enabled the young woman to accomplish something great. In the years that followed, Emily Dickinson wrote 1,775 poems!

**Emily Dickinson
(1830–1886)**

Listen to this passage at vocabularyworkshop.com.

Sometimes, Emily might send a poem to a friend, but she didn't try to publish her poetry. If anything, she concealed it, tying her poems in bundles and hiding them in her dresser drawers.

Fortunately, Emily's poetry didn't stay hidden from the world. After her death, the poems were finally published. When they appeared in print, readers couldn't believe how rich—and vast—her output had been. Although she never left the shelter of her house, Emily Dickinson had a keen imagination. In a drop of water, she could see a flood; in a grain of sand, she saw a desert.

To write so many poems, Emily Dickinson must have experienced many spurts of inspiration. Yet she crafted each poem carefully, choosing the exact words, rhythms, and punctuation to express her meaning. Some of the poems do reflect her loneliness, but they are inspiring too. Somehow, Dickinson could use a simple image—the wind in the trees, a robin on a garden path, a train in the valley—to suggest life's endless possibilities.

Simply put, Emily Dickinson was one of America's finest poets. From the stillness of her quiet room in Amherst, her delicate yet powerful words echoed across the land.

Emily Dickinson's home is now a museum.

Definitions

You were introduced to the words below in the passage on pages 56–57. Study the pronunciation, spelling, part of speech, and definition of each word. Write the word in the blank space in the sentence that follows. Then read the synonyms and antonyms.

1. accomplish
(ə käm′ plish)

(v.) to do, make happen, succeed in, carry through

Let's work together to _____ the task.

SYNONYMS: to perform, fulfill, achieve, complete
ANTONYMS: to fail, undo, fall short

2. apparent
(ə par′ ənt)

(adj.) open to view; easy to understand; seeming to be true or real

Speeding was the _____ cause of the accident.

SYNONYMS: clear, obvious, visible; plain; likely
ANTONYMS: hidden, concealed; difficult, uncertain

3. capacity
(kə pa′ sə tē)

(n.) the amount of space that can be filled; ability or skill; office or role

The stadium was filled to _____ for the championship game.

SYNONYMS: volume, size, room; gift; position, job

4. civilian
(sə vil′ yən)

(n.) a person not in a military, police, or firefighting force

A team of _____ investigated the accident.

(adj.) nonmilitary

No _____ casualties were reported.

SYNONYM: (n. & adj.) nonmilitary
ANTONYM: (n. & adj.) military

5. conceal
(kən sēl′)

(v.) to hide or keep secret, to place out of sight

I tried to _____ my disappointment with a smile.

SYNONYMS: to cover, disguise, mask, tuck away
ANTONYMS: to uncover, open, reveal

6. duplicate
(v., dü′ pli kāt;
n., adj., dü′ pli kət)

(v.) to copy exactly; to produce something equal to

A locksmith can _____ almost any key.

(adj.) exactly like something else

My friend and I came up with _____ plans.

((n.) an exact copy

He hung up a framed _____
of a famous painting in his office.

SYNONYMS: (v.) to reproduce, clone; (adj.) identical;
(n.) a reproduction, replica
ANTONYM: (n.) an original

7. keen
(kēn)

(adj.) having a sharpened edge; quick and
sharp in thought or in sight, hearing, or smell; eager

Birds of prey have _____ eyesight.

SYNONYMS: razor-edged; acute, alert; ready
ANTONYMS: dull, blunt; lazy, unwilling

8. provoke
(prə vōk')

(v.) to annoy or make angry, stir up; to do something in order to get a
response

Name-calling is bound to _____ an argument.

SYNONYMS: to excite, enrage, madden, goad
ANTONYMS: to calm, soothe, pacify, quiet

9. spurt
(spûrt)

(v.) to shoot out quickly in a stream; to show a burst of energy

We watched the runners _____ for the finish line.

(n.) a sudden, short stream of fluid; a quick burst of activity

My shirt was stained by a _____ of ketchup.

SYNONYMS: (v.) to squirt, gush, flow; (n.) a jet, surge

10. undoing
(ən dü' iŋ)

(n.) a bringing to ruin or destruction; the cause of ruin; unfastening or
loosening

Idle gossip was the cause of their _____.

SYNONYMS: downfall, misfortune, trouble; an opening
ANTONYMS: good luck, fortune, success; fastening

11. vast
(vast)

(adj.) very great or very large

A _____ ocean stretched into the distance.

SYNONYMS: huge, enormous, spacious
ANTONYMS: tiny, small, little, narrow

12. withdraw
(with drô')

(v.) to pull out or remove; to move back or away, retreat

Is it too late to _____ from the race?

SYNONYMS: to subtract; to leave, depart
ANTONYMS: to deposit, enter; to attack

Match the Meaning

vocabularyworkshop.com **Practice** unit words with interactive games and activities.

For each item below, choose the word whose meaning is suggested by the clue given. Then write the word in the space provided.

1. Your teacher might use a copier to _____ an assignment.
   a. provoke   b. duplicate   c. accomplish   d. spurt

2. A person who is not part of the military is a(n) _____.
   a. civilian   b. capacity   c. spurt   d. undoing

3. To remove something is to _____ it.
   a. provoke   b. conceal   c. withdraw   d. duplicate

4. The number of people who can fit into a room depends upon its _____.
   a. capacity   b. spurts   c. duplicates   d. civilians

5. Something that seems obvious is said to be _____.
   a. keen   b. vast   c. apparent   d. civilian

6. A(n) _____ from a garden hose might get you wet.
   a. undoing   b. duplicate   c. spurt   d. capacity

7. A(n) _____ blade will cut much better than a dull one.
   a. keen   b. apparent   c. vast   d. civilian

8. If you tease someone, you might _____ that person.
   a. accomplish   b. conceal   c. provoke   d. withdraw

9. A serious mistake might lead to one's _____.
   a. capacity   b. spurt   c. civilian   d. undoing

10. To hide something is to _____ it.
   a. accomplish   b. conceal   c. provoke   d. withdraw

11. The Atlantic Ocean is a(n) _____ body of water.
   a. keen   b. duplicate   c. apparent   d. vast

12. When you reach your goal, you have _____ something.
   a. concealed   b. withdrawn   c. duplicated   d. accomplished

The partygoers wore masks to **conceal** their identities.

Synonyms

*For each item below, choose the word that is most nearly the **same** in meaning as the word or phrase in **boldface**. Then write your choice on the line provided.*

1. create an **identical** set of plans

    a. vast   b. duplicate   c. keen   d. apparent   _____

2. measured the trunk's **room**

    a. capacity   b. spurt   c. civilian   d. undoing   _____

3. complete the mission in two weeks

    a. provoke   b. duplicate   c. accomplish   d. withdraw   _____

4. led to the **downfall** of the dictator

    a. civilian   b. spurt   c. capacity   d. undoing   _____

5. depart from the battlefield

    a. withdraw   b. provoke   c. spurt   d. conceal   _____

6. water that **squirted** from the hose

    a. concealed   b. spurted   c. withdrew   d. provoked   _____

Antonyms

*For each item below, choose the word that is most nearly **opposite** in meaning to the word or phrase in **boldface**. Then write your choice on the line provided.*

1. hidden reasons

    a. apparent   b. keen   c. vast   d. civilian   _____

2. a **military** operation

    a. vast   b. civilian   c. apparent   d. keen   _____

3. a **small** field

    a. keen   b. duplicate   c. civilian   d. vast   _____

4. calm the animal

    a. provoke   b. conceal   c. duplicate   d. accomplish   _____

5. reveal the answers

    a. duplicate   b. provoke   c. conceal   d. withdraw   _____

6. a **dull** sense of humor

    a. vast   b. civilian   c. duplicate   d. keen   _____

Completing the Sentence

Choose the word from the box that best completes each item below. Then write the word in the space provided. (You may have to change the word's ending.)

accomplish	apparent	capacity
civilian	conceal	duplicate
keen	provoke	spurt
undoing	vast	withdraw

Revolution in America and France

■ One of the events that led to the American Revolution was the Boston Massacre, when British soldiers fired into a crowd of _____.

■ Some historians say that the soldiers were _____ into firing by the insults and taunts of the crowd.

■ It soon became _____ to the British—even those who preferred not to see it—that the American colonies would settle for nothing less than full independence.

■ The leaders of the French Revolution were inspired by the American Revolution and hoped to _____ its success.

■ The Revolution in France led to the death of King Louis and the _____ of the old order.

A California Desert

■ With an area of 25,000 square miles, the Mojave Desert covers a(n)

_____ portion of southern California. On the desert's border is Death Valley, the lowest point in North America.

■ During the daytime some animals, such as the kangaroo rat, _____ from the hot desert floor to cooler underground burrows.

■ Though the desert roadrunner is a poor flier, it can run in quick _____ to capture its prey. The roadrunner feeds on lizards, snakes, and insects.

The Sixteenth President

■ In his _____ as commander in chief, Abraham Lincoln played an important part in choosing the generals of the Union armies.

■ General Ulysses S. Grant _____ what no other Union general before him had been able to do—force the surrender of Robert E. Lee.

■ Lincoln's aides so feared for his safety that they often went to great lengths to

_____ his movements.

■ The many examples of his jokes and stories show that Lincoln possessed a(n)

_____ sense of humor.

Word Study • Suffixes -ment, -ance, -age, -hood

A **suffix** is a word part that is added to the end of a **base word** to make a new word. Remember that base words are complete and make sense as independent words. You can add the suffix -ment to accomplish (page 58) to make a new word.

> The suffixes **-ment, -ance,** and **-age** mean "the act, state, or result of."
> accomplish + **ment** = accomplish**ment** → means "an achievement"
> assist + **ance** = assist**ance** → means "help that is given"
> pack + **age** = pack**age** → means "a parcel"
>
> The suffix **-hood** means "the state, quality, or condition of."
> false + **hood** = false**hood** → means "an untrue statement"

PRACTICE *Write the missing base word, suffix, or new word. Then write the meaning of the new word. Use a dictionary to check your answers.*

Base Word	Suffix	New Word	Meaning
1. _____	+ ment	= statement	→ _____
2. disturb	+ _____	= disturbance	→ _____
3. pass	+ age	= _____	→ _____
4. _____	+ hood	= neighborhood	→ _____

APPLY *Complete each sentence with a word that contains the suffix -ment, -ance, -age, or -hood. Choose from the words above.*

5. The mail carrier delivered the _____ that I sent to my aunt.

6. A _____ that is not the truth is a _____.

7. My greatest _____ was winning the school spelling bee.

8. In our _____ of thirty houses, we give _____ to the senior citizens who live there.

Add a suffix to each word below to make a new word. Choose from -ment, -ance, -age, and -hood. Then use the new word in a sentence. Use a dictionary if you need help.

9. amaze _____ _____

10. orphan _____ _____

11. attend _____ _____

12. boy _____ _____

Vocabulary for Comprehension

*Read the following passage in which some of the words you have studied in Units 4–6 appear in **boldface**. Then answer the questions on page 65.*

Trouble in Paradise

Far from anywhere, in the middle of the **vast** Pacific Ocean, lies the beautiful island nation of Nauru. Sandy beaches, swaying palm trees, and clear blue water circle the island. Some even claim that this isolated country is paradise.

Nauru is one of the smallest nations on Earth. It is only about 8 square miles in size. It is home to only about 14,000 people. Nauru used to be very rich. This was because its land held a lot of phosphate. Phosphate is a natural material used for farming and making new products. The phosphate on Nauru formed from droppings of birds flying by! People dug this unusual treasure from the ground. Then they loaded it onto ships for **transport** around the world.

The **aggressive** digging and selling of phosphate made Nauru very rich. For a while, its people were some of the richest in the world. Unfortunately, the digging also destroyed Nauru's land. Then around the year 2000, the phosphate ran out. Suddenly, this tiny country had a big problem. Not only was its land ruined, but it also had no way to earn money.

Today, the people of Nauru struggle to build a new future for their country. They have many ideas. One idea is to attract visitors in search of a **luxurious** beach vacation. Visitors might bring money, and their presence might create new jobs for Nauru's residents. This will be a hard goal to **accomplish** because the island is so far away from most places. However, the people of Nauru hope their tiny, beautiful island and their **hospitality** will encourage others to vacation there.

Fill in the circle next to the choice that best completes the sentence or answers the question.

1. The meaning of **vast** is
   - (a) very large.
   - (b) dangerous.
   - (c) cold.
   - (d) important.

2. In this passage, **transport** means
   - (a) the process of moving things.
   - (b) the process of destroying land.
   - (c) a large land vehicle.
   - (d) to dig out of the ground.

3. Another word for **aggressive** is
   - (a) weak.
   - (b) determined.
   - (c) useless.
   - (d) angry.

4. What happened to much of the land on Nauru?
   - (a) It was destroyed by birds.
   - (b) It became great for farming.
   - (c) It was destroyed by digging.
   - (d) It no longer has beautiful beaches.

5. In this passage, **luxurious** means
   - (a) frightening.
   - (b) very pleasurable.
   - (c) very cheap.
   - (d) extremely unpleasant.

6. Another word for **accomplish** is
   - (a) fail.
   - (b) understand.
   - (c) achieve.
   - (d) withdraw.

7. In this passage, the meaning of **hospitality** is
   - (a) friendliness.
   - (b) illness.
   - (c) hostility.
   - (d) distance.

8. This passage was mainly written to
   - (a) tell a funny story.
   - (b) describe where phosphate comes from.
   - (c) describe an island country and its problems.
   - (d) encourage people to take vacations in Nauru.

Write Your Own

Many people in Nauru want to encourage travelers to vacation on their island. Imagine you are writing a travel brochure for the area you live in. Write to persuade others to come visit. Use at least three words from Units 4–6.

Classifying

Choose the word from the box that goes best with each group of words. Write the word in the space provided. Then explain what the words have in common. The first one has been done for you.

bluff	capacity	cautious
conceal	~~continuous~~	detect
document	hazy	monarch
productive	supreme	vast

1. continue, continual, _____continuous_____, continuation

The words belong to the same word family. _____

2. blunt, _____, blood, blanket, blade

_____

3. crazy, daisy, _____, lazy

_____

4. enormous, immense, massive, _____

_____

5. spot, observe, notice, _____

_____

6. article, essay, report, _____

_____

7. produce, product, _____, production

_____

8. horrible, mediocre, good, _____

_____

9. president, dictator, emperor, _____

_____

10. mask, hide, disguise, _____

_____

11. reckless, daring, wild, _____

_____

12. length, width, weight, _____

_____

Completing the Idea

Complete each sentence so that it makes sense. Pay attention to the word in **boldface.**

1. When I clean a **fragile** vase, I _____.

2. To **justify** my opinion, I _____.

3. My favorite meal **consists** of _____.

4. We were able to **overwhelm** the other team because _____.

5. To prepare for the **festive** event, we _____.

6. A dog with a **keen** sense of smell can _____.

7. Our class had to **cancel** our trip because _____.

8. In order to settle our **dispute**, we _____.

9. Whenever I face an **obstacle**, I _____.

10. A **flexible** person is able to _____.

11. A **miniature** train set takes up _____.

12. I had to **withdraw** from the competition because _____.

13. The **veteran** spoke to our class about _____.

14. The advertisement is **misleading** because _____.

15. Whenever a **mishap** occurs, I try to _____.

16. The athlete felt **fatigue** after _____.

17. The **apparent** cause of the fire was _____.

Writing Challenge

Write two sentences using the word **associate.** *In the first sentence, use* **associate** *as a verb. In the second sentence, use* **associate** *as an adjective.*

1. _____

2. _____

Introducing the Words

Read the following biography about the career and travels of a modern-day explorer. Notice how the highlighted words are used. These are the words you will be learning in this unit.

Eugenie Clark: Swimming with Sharks

(Biography)

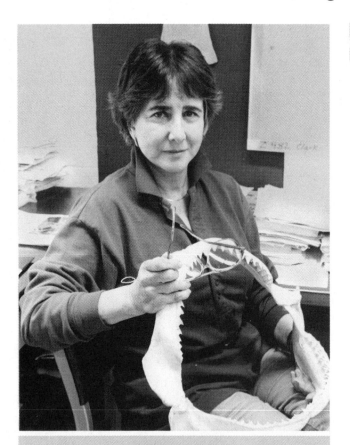

Dr. Eugenie Clark

Nine-year-old Genie leaned against the glass barrier and stared at the fish. This was her first visit to the aquarium, and she couldn't keep her eyes off the underwater scene. Neon fish flashed by, and an octopus waved. Genie, however, stared mainly at the sharks. Imagine swimming with these graceful creatures!

After that, Genie became a reliable visitor to the New York City Aquarium. She went back week after week, always learning more about ocean life. Soon she decided to become an *ichthyologist*, a scientist who studies fish. She was only in fourth grade, but Eugenie Clark calculated that there was nothing else that she would rather do than swim with the sharks.

Years later, Genie's dream came true, when, in her twenties, she became Dr. Eugenie Clark. She had degrees in marine biology and experience studying fish all over the world. Since diving was the best way to study fish, Dr. Clark obtained some scuba gear. On one early dive, a large shark appeared and gave her a jolt. Not frightened, Clark simply admired the shark's beauty.

Swimming with sharks was fun, but Eugenie Clark also wanted to learn about them through experiments. To pursue this kind of work, she started a marine laboratory in Florida. Doing so made her the first woman in the United States to run her own marine biology lab, a considerable achievement.

Over the years, Clark composed many articles and even wrote a book about her adventures that was called *The Lady and the Sharks*. The book became a best-seller, and people started calling her "Shark Lady." Clark also helped teach people about ocean life through films and television shows. Always on the go, she did not appoint deputies to do the filming. Instead, she traveled the world to take part in it herself.

During her travels, Clark often called attention to threats to the ocean environment. For example, she often dived in the Red Sea in Egypt. There, the Ras Muhammad reefs, like many of the world's coral reefs, were being harmed by pollution. To save the reefs, Eugenie Clark teamed with Egyptian scientists and divers. Together, these experts made the Egyptian government and public aware of the problem. Many Egyptians rejoiced when, as a result of their efforts, Ras Muhammad became Egypt's first national park.

Eugenie Clark wasn't about to retire when she turned sixty-five. Instead, she began to dive in submersibles, or mini-submarines. For Clark, the subs safely opened up new areas of the ocean for study. After all, diving deep down or for long periods of time in scuba gear can be unhealthy and dangerous. Exposure to salt water can shrivel a person's skin. The intense pressure of the water can leave a diver unconscious and senseless. By contrast, a diver in a submersible can descend thousands of feet with no harmful physical effects.

Industrious as ever, Dr. Clark keeps studying sharks and writing books. Diving in submersibles, she continues to live her childhood dream of exploring the treasures of the sea. To her, of course, that doesn't mean sunken treasure chests and pirate loot, but rather the wonders of underwater life.

In Australia, Dr. Clark swam with a whale shark, the world's largest shark.

Definitions

You were introduced to the words below in the passage on pages 68–69. Study the pronunciation, spelling, part of speech, and definition of each word. Write the word in the blank space in the sentence that follows. Then read the synonyms and antonyms.

1. barrier
(bar′ ē ər)

(n.) something that blocks the way; an obstacle

Firefighters often construct a _____ to stop a forest fire.

SYNONYMS: an obstruction, fence, wall, blockade, safeguard
ANTONYMS: an opening, passage

2. calculate
(kal′ kyə lāt)

(v.) to find out by using mathematics or reasoning; to reckon, estimate

The math teacher asked us to _____ the number of hours we spend on homework each week.

SYNONYMS: to gauge, figure, determine, judge

3. compose
(kəm pōz′)

(v.) to be or make up the parts of, form; to create or write; to calm or quiet one's mind

Before you _____ the essay, you might write an outline.

SYNONYMS: to produce, invent; to still, settle
ANTONYMS: to annoy, disturb

4. considerable
(kən sid′ ər ə bəl)

(adj.) fairly large in size or extent; worthy of attention

It will take a _____ amount of time to complete the science project.

SYNONYMS: great, sizable, major, important
ANTONYMS: small, slight, negligible

5. deputy
(de′ pyə tē)

(n.) one chosen to help or take the place of another or to act in that person's absence

The sheriff's first act after winning the election was to appoint a

_____ .

SYNONYMS: an assistant, aide, substitute

6. industrious
(in dus′ trē əs)

(adj.) busy, working steadily

The crew that gathered to clean up the vacant lot was as

_____ as an ant colony.

SYNONYMS: active, occupied, energetic, untiring
ANTONYMS: lazy, idle, loafing, slow

7. jolt
(jōlt)

(v.) to shake up roughly; to move along in a jerky or bumpy fashion

It was fun to _____ *down the dirt road in the wagon.*

(n.) a sudden bump or jerk; a shock or surprise

We felt a _____ *as the Ferris wheel started.*

SYNONYMS: (v.) to jar, rattle, hit; (n.) a lurch, bounce

8. loot
(lüt)

(v.) to rob by force or violence, especially during war or time of unrest

The soldiers were warned not to _____ *the villages.*

(n.) valuable things that have been stolen or taken by force

Detectives found _____ *from a dozen robberies.*

SYNONYMS: (v.) to steal, plunder; (n.) prize, spoils

9. rejoice
(ri jois')

(v.) to feel joy or great delight; to make joyful

The whole town will _____ *if the team wins the championship.*

SYNONYMS: to celebrate, cheer
ANTONYMS: to grieve, mourn

10. reliable
(re lī' ə bəl)

(adj.) deserving trust, dependable

It is not easy to find a _____ *baby-sitter.*

SYNONYMS: faithful, proven, trustworthy
ANTONYMS: unreliable, questionable, fickle

11. senseless
(sens' ləs)

(adj.) lacking meaning, stupid or foolish; without use of the senses

The boxer was knocked _____ *by the blow.*

SYNONYMS: ridiculous, silly, illogical, birdbrained; unconscious
ANTONYMS: brilliant, clever, smart

12. shrivel
(shriv' əl)

(v.) to shrink and wrinkle, especially from heat, cold, or dryness

Exposed skin will _____ *in the frosty air.*

SYNONYMS: to wither, dry, contract
ANTONYMS: to expand, enlarge, swell

Match the Meaning

vocabularyworkshop.com **Practice** unit words with interactive games and activities.

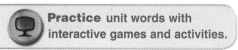

For each item below, choose the word whose meaning is suggested by the clue given. Then write the word in the space provided.

1. _____ people always stay busy by finding things to do.
   a. considerable   b. senseless   c. reliable   d. industrious

2. Because we forgot to water the plants, they all _____.
   a. composed   b. shriveled   c. calculated   d. rejoiced

3. When I ride my bike on an unpaved road, I feel a _____ with each bump.
   a. jolt   b. loot   c. deputy   d. barrier

4. An action without meaning may be called _____.
   a. industrious   b. considerable   c. senseless   d. reliable

5. Something that poses an obstacle is called a _____.
   a. jolt   b. deputy   c. loot   d. barrier

6. Add the cost of all the food and drinks, as well as the tax and tip, to _____ the total cost of the meal.
   a. jolt   b. calculate   c. rejoice   d. compose

7. A person chosen to act in another's absence is a _____.
   a. deputy   b. loot   c. jolt   d. barrier

8. Calm yourself and quiet your mind to _____ your thoughts.
   a. calculate   b. rejoice   c. compose   d. jolt

9. A(n) _____ number is a pretty large one.
   a. reliable   b. industrious   c. considerable   d. senseless

10. A(n) _____ car starts up every morning, even in winter.
   a. industrious   b. senseless   c. considerable   d. reliable

11. To celebrate with delight is to _____.
   a. shrivel   b. rejoice   c. calculate   d. compose

12. The robbers stashed their _____ in an old refrigerator.
   a. loot   b. barrier   c. deputy   d. jolt

The robber was caught carrying the **loot** he had stolen.

Synonyms

*For each item below, choose the word that is most nearly the **same** in meaning as the word or phrase in **boldface**. Then write your choice on the line provided.*

1. knocked **unconscious** when I fell off the ladder

a. industrious   b. senseless   c. considerable   d. reliable   _____

2. jarred by the rough landing

a. jolted   b. composed   c. shriveled   d. looted   _____

3. produce a long poem

a. jolt   b. calculate   c. compose   d. rejoice   _____

4. call the **assistant** for help

a. barrier   b. loot   c. deputy   d. jolt   _____

5. determine the cost of painting the apartment

a. compose   b. rejoice   c. jolt   d. calculate   _____

6. would **plunder** the house while the owners were away

a. jolt   b. compose   c. loot   d. calculate   _____

Antonyms

*For each item below, choose the word that is most nearly **opposite** in meaning to the word or phrase in **boldface**. Then write your choice on the line provided.*

1. the **idle** carpenter

a. considerable   b. industrious   c. reliable   d. senseless   _____

2. swell in the heat

a. calculate   b. jolt   c. compose   d. shrivel   _____

3. mourn over the election results

a. loot   b. calculate   c. rejoice   d. shrivel   _____

4. made a **slight** difference

a. considerable   b. industrious   c. senseless   d. reliable   _____

5. a **questionable** source of information

a. industrious   b. considerable   c. reliable   d. senseless   _____

6. found an **opening**

a. deputy   b. loot   c. jolt   d. barrier   _____

Completing the Sentence

Choose the word from the box that best completes each item below. Then write the word in the space provided. (You may have to change the word's ending.)

barrier	calculate	compose
considerable	deputy	industrious
jolt	loot	rejoice
reliable	senseless	shrivel

Earthquake!

■ The powerful earthquake that hit the San Francisco Bay area on October 17, 1989, did _____ damage to the city, though not nearly so much as was done by the terrible earthquake and fire of 1906.

■ The mighty _____, which registered 7.1 on the Richter scale, shook buildings and buckled elevated highways.

■ Safety officials put up _____ to keep people away from unsafe areas.

■ Scientists _____ that the loss of life and property would have been far greater if the earthquake had hit during the day instead of early evening.

A Great Artist

■ The Dutch painter Vincent van Gogh was an ambitious and _____ artist who made hundreds of paintings and drawings during his short lifetime. He moved to southern France in 1888, and there he produced many of his masterpieces. Van Gogh died in 1890 at the age of 37.

■ Van Gogh _____ at the completion of each new painting but despaired that his work never sold.

■ As the summer heat _____ the olives on the trees near his home, van Gogh wrote sad letters to his brother Theo.

■ He _____ works of great beauty that were not appreciated until after his death. Today his paintings are in museums all over the world and are sold for millions of dollars.

Sirens in the Night

■ When a power blackout darkened part of the city, some criminals roamed the streets. They broke windows and _____ neighborhood stores.

■ Community leaders spoke out against this _____ violence and urged people to act responsibly during the emergency.

■ Several sheriff's _____ arrived to restore order and interview witnesses.

■ One witness offered information about the robberies, but the police officers paid him little mind because they knew he was not _____.

Word Associations

Circle the letter next to the word or expression that best completes the sentence or answers the question. Pay special attention to the word in **boldface.**

1. Which is a **barrier** to success in school?
   a. poor study habits
   b. weak stomach muscles
   c. a tall fence
   d. no brothers or sisters

2. An **industrious** person could
   a. build a hen house in ten years.
   b. build a dollhouse in five years.
   c. build a birdhouse in one year.
   d. build a doghouse in one day.

3. A **deputy** would probably carry
   a. a badge.
   b. a bag lunch.
   c. a wrench.
   d. a banner.

4. It is **senseless** to try to count
   a. to one thousand.
   b. change after a purchase.
   c. grains of sand at the beach.
   d. people ahead of you in line.

5. You might **rejoice** if you
   a. found your lost dog.
   b. ruined your favorite shirt.
   c. failed a spelling test.
   d. saw the latest comedy film.

6. Which is a **considerable** sum?
   a. 30¢
   b. $1.00
   c. $5.00
   d. $5,000.00

7. If you **compose** your autobiography, you will be
   a. driving a new car.
   b. writing the story of your life.
   c. interviewing strangers.
   d. making up a new song.

8. You might feel **jolted** by
   a. a good night's sleep.
   b. a delicious lunch.
   c. shocking news.
   d. yesterday's paper.

9. People guilty of **looting** are
   a. winning a prize.
   b. breaking the law.
   c. running in circles.
   d. taking pictures.

10. A balloon would quickly **shrivel**
    a. if air leaks from it.
    b. if it floats away.
    c. if it gets wet.
    d. if it is tied to a string.

11. A **reliable** friend is one who
    a. doesn't let you down.
    b. makes fun of you.
    c. is never on time.
    d. always makes you laugh.

12. Which might be used to **calculate**?
    a. an alarm clock
    b. paper and pencil
    c. a hammer
    d. knife and fork

Word Study • Prefixes *pre-, in-, im-, ir-, il-*

A **prefix** is a word part that is added to the beginning of a **base word** to make a new word. You can add the prefix *pre-* to *calculate* (page 70) to make a new word.

> The prefix **pre-** means "before."
> **pre** + calculate = **pre**calculate → means "calculate before"
>
> ---
>
> The prefixes **in-, im-, ir-,** and **il-** often mean "not" or "without."
> **in** + capable = **in**capable → means "not have the ability to"
> **im** + mobile = **im**mobile → means "not able to move"
> **ir** + replaceable = **ir**replaceable → means "cannot be replaced"
> **il** + legal = **il**legal → means "not legal"

PRACTICE *Write the missing prefix and base word. Then write the meaning of the new word.*

Prefix	Base Word	New Word	Meaning
1. _____ + _____		= improper →	_____
2. _____ + _____		= incomplete →	_____
3. _____ + _____		= irrelevant →	_____
4. _____ + _____		= illegible →	_____
5. _____ + _____		= predate →	_____

APPLY *Complete each sentence with a word that contains the prefix* pre-, in-, im-, ir, *or* il-. *Choose from the words above.*

6. My teacher said my messy handwriting was _____.

7. The phones in our house _____ the cell phone that I carry.

8. After I broke my leg, I was _____ for a few weeks.

9. I tried not to include any _____ details in my report.

10. My brother was _____ of giving me a good reason for skipping breakfast.

11. It is _____ to talk while someone is giving a speech.

Write two words that begin with each of the prefixes **pre-, in-, im-, ir-,** *and* **il-.** *Then consult a dictionary, either in a book or online, to check the meanings.*

Shades of Meaning • Metaphors

In the passage "Eugenie Clark: Swimming with Sharks" on pages 68–69, you read about Eugenie Clark's love of fish, especially the shark, and her love of the ocean environment. She loved swimming with the ocean's creatures and exploring their world. To Eugenie, these creatures and their surroundings ***are treasures of the sea***. In this sentence, *are treasures of the sea* is a metaphor.

A **metaphor** compares two unlike things without using the words *like* or *as*. A metaphor doesn't say that one thing is *like* another. It says that one thing *is* another. Saying that the ocean's creatures and their surroundings *are treasures of the sea* means that the ocean's creatures and their surroundings are amazing underwater sights.

PRACTICE *Read each sentence. Figure out the meaning of each metaphor in* **boldface***. Write the number of each sentence next to its meaning.*

1. The assignment **was a breeze**. I was able to finish it in only ten minutes.

2. These lovely earrings **are twinkling stars**.

3. I eat so much that my mother thinks my stomach is **a bottomless pit**.

4. The boom of fireworks **was thunder in the night**. It could be heard a mile away.

_____ very loud

_____ easy

_____ sparkly

_____ without end or limit

APPLY *Read each sentence. Figure out the meaning of each metaphor in* **boldface***. Write the meaning on the line provided.*

5. The shopping center **was a sea of people**.

_____

6. During the heat of the summer, the attic **is a sauna**.

_____

7. By the time we unpacked our camping gear, the garage **was a disaster area**.

_____

8. Even though they are brothers, their personalities **are night and day**.

_____

9. On election night, the candidate's office was **a whirlwind of activity**.

_____

Introducing the Words

Read the following essay about a building from New York City's past. Notice how the highlighted words are used. These are the words you will be learning in this unit.

What Happened to Pennsylvania Station?

(Essay)

Cars and taxis passed the eighty-four pink granite columns that stood like guards at the front of the station. Pedestrians approached along an elegant arched passageway. The waiting room was fifteen stories high and a block and a half long. In many ways, Pennsylvania Station, also known as Penn Station, was the heart of New York City.

Built in 1910, the station was an energetic place. Filled with bustling crowds, Penn Station welcomed travelers with its bright and hearty atmosphere. Getting on or off a train here was an exciting thing to do.

By the 1950s, however, fewer people were traveling by train. They had found alternate ways to travel. Airlines carried more and more passengers. New superhighways made driving long distances easier.

By the end of the decade, the owners of Penn Station made a fateful decision. They would demolish the famous landmark. In its

The Clock in Penn Station was a popular meeting place.

place, they would build an office building and a sports arena. The plan seemed to make financial sense, but little thought was given to train passengers. People would now have to board trains underground from small waiting areas near the train tunnels.

Demolish Penn Station? When New Yorkers heard the plan, they couldn't believe their ears. One of the city's finest public places had been given a death sentence, and New Yorkers didn't like the verdict!

Citizens joined together to save the landmark. For months, they would strive to rescue it from the wrecking ball. They pointed out that the station was an architectural treasure. It had played a key role in the life and history of the city. What's more, the new underground station would be cramped and uncomfortable. A person didn't have to be very observant to see that.

Unfortunately, no one could stop the tragedy. City officials enforced the wishes of the owners, and in 1963, the wrecking balls went to work. Onlookers gazed in horror as an architectural masterpiece crashed to the ground in dust.

In the end, New Yorkers resigned themselves to the loss of Penn Station. They had, however, learned a lesson: Landmark buildings had to be saved. A special landmarks commission was formed. Its primary purpose was to identify and protect the city's finest architecture. Its

members recognized that as a city changes and matures, some older buildings do have to be demolished to make room for new ones. Landmarks, however, must be preserved.

Ironically, by the 1990s, train travel had picked up at Penn Station, especially among commuters from surrounding towns. The underground station had difficulty handling the raging river of traffic. As predicted, few liked the cramped replacement.

Some New Yorkers hope to convert a grand old post office into a new train station. The post office is in the right place, and in some ways, it resembles the old Pennsylvania Station. The plan may work, but the overhaul will be a very difficult and costly feat. So the tragedy teaches another lesson: Sometimes, it's better to preserve what we have than to try to replace it.

Main Waiting Room at Pennsylvania Station

Pennsylvania Station was one of New York City's most beautiful structures.

Definitions

You were introduced to the words below in the passage on pages 78–79. Study the pronunciation, spelling, part of speech, and definition of each word. Write the word in the blank space in the sentence that follows. Then read the synonyms and antonyms.

1. alternate
(v., ôl′ tər nāt;
n., adj., ôl′ tər nət)

(v.) to do, use, or happen in successive turns; to take turns

We chose two students to _____ in the lead role for our class play.

(n.) a person acting or prepared to act in place of another; a substitute

Juries usually include two or more _____.

(adj.) happening or appearing in turns; every other; being a choice between two or more things

The bus driver took an _____ route.

SYNONYMS: (v.) to rotate, change; (n.) a replacement, deputy

2. demolish
(di mäl′ ish)

(v.) to tear down, break to pieces

A wrecking crew arrived to _____ the old building.

SYNONYMS: to raze, destroy, wreck, smash, level
ANTONYMS: to construct, build, restore, mend

3. energetic
(e nər je′ tik)

(adj.) active and vigorous, full of energy, forceful

Our teacher has an _____ assistant.

SYNONYMS: hardworking, tireless, peppy
ANTONYMS: idle, lazy, inactive

4. enforce
(en fôrs′)

(v.) to force obedience to

It is the duty of the police to protect citizens and _____ the laws.

SYNONYM: to carry out
ANTONYMS: to overlook, abandon, disregard

5. feat
(fēt)

(n.) an act or deed that shows daring, skill, or strength

The crowd cheered when the circus strongman performed a mighty _____.

SYNONYMS: an achievement, exploit, effort

6. hearty
(härt' ē)

(adj.) warm and friendly; healthy, lively, and strong; large and satisfying to the appetite

We all sat down to a _____ meal.

SYNONYMS: cheerful, friendly; fit, healthy; plentiful
ANTONYMS: insincere, phony; sickly

7. mature
(mə tûr')

(v.) to bring to or reach full development or growth

The puppy will _____ over the summer.

(adj.) fully grown or developed

A field of _____ oats waved in the breeze.

SYNONYMS: (v.) to grow, develop, age, ripen; (adj.) complete, ripe
ANTONYMS: (adj.) immature, inexperienced, raw, green

8. observant
(əb zûr' vənt)

(adj.) watchful, quick to notice; careful and diligent

An _____ guard spotted the vandals.

SYNONYMS: aware, attentive, alert, sharp; dutiful, mindful
ANTONYMS: inattentive, careless

9. primary
(prī' mer ē)

(adj.) first in importance, first in time or order; basic, fundamental

Raising money was our _____ order of business.

(n.) an early election that narrows the choice of candidates who will run in a final election

The challenger won the _____.

SYNONYMS: (adj.) highest, main, prime
ANTONYMS: (adj.) secondary, last

10. resign
(ri zīn')

(v.) to give up a job, an office, or a right or claim

Richard Nixon was the first President to _____ from office.

SYNONYMS: to quit, abandon, leave, surrender

11. strive
(strīv)

(v.) to devote much energy or effort, try hard

You must _____ to finish your homework on time.

SYNONYMS: to attempt, struggle, labor, slave, strain

12. verdict
(vûr' dikt)

(n.) the decision of a jury at the end of a trial or legal case; any decision

The jury brought in a guilty _____.

SYNONYMS: a ruling, judgment, finding

Match the Meaning

vocabularyworkshop.com

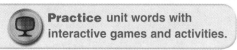

Practice unit words with interactive games and activities.

For each item below, choose the word whose meaning is suggested by the clue given. Then write the word in the space provided.

1. To make people obey laws is to _____ those laws.
   a. enforce   b. alternate   c. demolish   d. strive

2. To break something to pieces is to _____ it.
   a. alternate   b. demolish   c. resign   d. mature

3. An amazing act or deed might be called a(n) _____.
   a. feat   b. verdict   c. primary   d. alternate

4. On cold mornings, my favorite breakfast is a(n) _____ bowl of hot oatmeal with brown sugar, cinnamon, and walnuts.
   a. mature   b. observant   c. hearty   d. primary

5. The decision that a jury gives at the end of a trial is called the

   _____.
   a. feat   b. primary   c. alternate   d. verdict

6. If you give up a job, you _____ from it.
   a. enforce   b. resign   c. mature   d. alternate

7. Something that is first in importance, first in time order, or first in

   another basic way is called _____.
   a. primary   b. mature   c. alternate   d. energetic

8. In most games, players take turns or _____ moves.
   a. resign   b. demolish   c. alternate   d. enforce

9. A frisky puppy can be described as _____.
   a. observant   b. energetic   c. mature   d. primary

10. If you are very _____, you'll notice the clues.
    a. primary   b. hearty   c. mature   d. observant

11. Once fruit is fully _____, it can be harvested.
    a. energetic   b. mature   c. hearty   d. alternate

12. To try very hard is to _____.
    a. strive   b. alternate   c. demolish   d. resign

Athletes are more likely to win medals if they perform a **feat** that impresses the judges.

Synonyms

*For each item below, choose the word that is most nearly the **same** in meaning as the word or phrase in **boldface**. Then write your choice on the line provided.*

1. handed down the **ruling**
   a. primary   b. feat   c. alternate   d. verdict   _____

2. a **cheerful** laugh that made his shoulders jiggle
   a. alternate   b. hearty   c. mature   d. observant   _____

3. read about the daring **achievement**
   a. feat   b. verdict   c. primary   d. alternate   _____

4. packed a **replacement** camera as a backup
   a. observant   b. hearty   c. primary   d. alternate   _____

5. **abandon** the job of manager
   a. alternate   b. demolish   c. strive   d. resign   _____

6. **attempt** to learn to read Japanese
   a. demolish   b. alternate   c. strive   d. resign   _____

Antonyms

*For each item below, choose the word that is most nearly **opposite** in meaning to the word or phrase in **boldface**. Then write your choice on the line provided.*

1. **construct** a covered bridge
   a. demolish   b. strive   c. alternate   d. enforce   _____

2. **idle** workers
   a. mature   b. energetic   c. observant   d. primary   _____

3. showed an **inexperienced** outlook
   a. alternate   b. hearty   c. mature   d. primary   _____

4. an **inattentive** reader
   a. alternate   b. mature   c. observant   d. hearty   _____

5. **overlook** the "No Smoking" laws
   a. alternate   b. strive   c. resign   d. enforce   _____

6. a **secondary** cause of blindness
   a. hearty   b. observant   c. primary   d. energetic   _____

Completing the Sentence

Choose the word from the box that best
completes each item below. Then write the
word in the space provided. (You may have
to change the word's ending.)

alternate	demolish	energetic
enforce	feat	hearty
mature	observant	primary
resign	strive	verdict

Raising a New House

■ The storm so badly damaged the house that it was unsafe to live in. The owner

decided to _____ it and build a new one.

■ It was quite a(n) _____ to tear down the house, clear the land, and
build another house in only ten weeks!

■ Two crews _____ in the building work. When one finished, the other
began, so that construction went on from break of day until after the sun went down.

■ All of the workers were encouraged to _____ as hard as they could to
finish the job ahead of schedule.

■ Luckily, a(n) _____ worker spotted a mistake in the building plans
before it caused a delay, and the house was finished on time. The worker was rewarded
for his attention and diligence.

An After-School Job

■ My sister says that the responsibilities of a part-time job can help teens develop into

more _____ individuals.

■ The managers at Burger Barn, where she works after school, _____
three rules: be on time, be honest, and be polite.

■ As long as she follows those rules, the managers greet her each day with a cheerful

smile and a _____ handshake.

To the Polls!

■ The _____ election in September decided which candidates would run
for state assembly in the general election in November. In the Democratic race, two
politicians challenged the two-term assemblyman for a place on the ballot.

■ All three candidates had the help of many young, _____ volunteers,
who worked tirelessly to get out the vote.

■ After ballots were counted, the _____ was clear: Voters wanted the
two-term assemblyman to run again.

■ However, health problems in October forced him to _____ his office
and pull out of the election.

Word Associations

*Circle the letter next to the word or expression that best completes the sentence or answers the question. Pay special attention to the word in **boldface**.*

1. Which is a **verdict**?

 a. "Thank you!"

 b. "Good morning!"

 c. "I told you so!"

 d. "Not guilty!"

2. If you and your sister **alternate** walking the dog, then you must

 a. do twice as much walking.

 b. walk the dog every other time.

 c. walk the dog two times in a row.

 d. walk farther than your sister.

3. Which is a firefighter's **feat**?

 a. polishing the fire trucks

 b. making daring rescues

 c. wearing waterproof boots

 d. cooking firehouse stew

4. Who would **enforce** a leash law?

 a. a scientist

 b. a weather forecaster

 c. a veterinarian

 d. a dogcatcher

5. People who **strive**

 a. give up easily.

 b. always succeed.

 c. do their very best.

 d. prefer to be outdoors.

6. Which is a **mature** animal?

 a. a sleepy puppy

 b. an old turtle

 c. a frisky kitten

 d. a new chick

7. An **energetic** performer might

 a. do three shows a day.

 b. nap during intermission.

 c. not answer fan mail.

 d. sing softly.

8. Which might be **resigned**?

 a. a greeting card

 b. a doctor's prescription

 c. a homework assignment

 d. a club membership

9. A **primary** concern is one that

 a. comes last.

 b. comes too late.

 c. comes first.

 d. comes when you least expect it.

10. Which might be **hearty**?

 a. a wink

 b. a laugh

 c. a sigh

 d. a whisper

11. If you are **observant**, you are

 a. wide awake.

 b. daydreaming.

 c. asleep.

 d. distracted.

12. Which would be the hardest to **demolish**?

 a. a snow fort

 b. a house made of cards

 c. a bookcase

 d. a dollhouse

Word Study • Using a Thesaurus

A **thesaurus** is a reference book that lists words with their synonyms. Sometimes it also lists antonyms. You can use a thesaurus to find more interesting or more exact words for a given word. Read this sentence: *The man will **leave** his job as a teacher to retire.* Then look at the thesaurus entry for *leave*. Look for a synonym that can replace *leave* to improve the sentence.

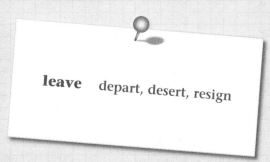

leave   depart, desert, resign

Think about the synonyms *depart* and *resign*. *Depart* means "to go away, typically to start a journey," and *resign* (page 81) means "to give up a job or position." Of these two synonyms, *resign* is the better replacement for *leave*.

PRACTICE *Look up each **boldface** entry word in a thesaurus. Then write two additional synonyms for the entry.*

1. **cold**   chilly, wintry, frosty,   _____ , _____

2. **make**   build, create, assemble,   _____ , _____

3. **surprise**   amaze, startle, astound,   _____ , _____

4. **leave**   depart, desert, resign,   _____ , _____

APPLY *Replace each **boldface** word with a synonym from the thesaurus entries above. Write the word on the line.*

5. It was **cold** the week before my swimming party. _____

6. If I accidentally drop a book, I will **surprise** the readers in the library.

_____

7. The artist likes to **make** works of art out of wire. _____

8. The buses **leave** the terminal at 9:10 P.M. _____

9. The weather turned **cold** as the autumn season came to an end.

_____

10. The gardener will **make** a shed for all her gardening tools. _____

Write a sentence about something that you did today. Then exchange sentences with a partner. Look for words in the sentence that could be more exact or more interesting. Use a thesaurus if you need to.

Shades of Meaning • Words That Describe People

In "What Happened to Pennsylvania Station?" on pages 78–79, you read a description about one of New York City's famous train stations. The text described it as an *energetic* place full of activity and an exciting place to be.

In the passage, *energetic* describes a place, but the word *energetic* can also describe a person. Look at the words in the chart. Learning the words will help you choose the right word to use when you describe people in speaking and writing.

energetic	People who are **energetic** are enthusiastic and full of energy.
finicky	People who are **finicky** are very fussy and difficult to please.
impatient	People who are **impatient** get annoyed easily, especially when waiting.
resourceful	People who are **resourceful** are clever and imaginative. They are effective, especially in difficult situations.

PRACTICE *Read each description. Choose a word from the chart to identify the type of person described.*

1. A person who participates in several after-school activities _____

2. A person who complains about standing in line _____

3. A person who is particular about how something is done _____

4. A person who is able to solve a problem creatively _____

5. A person who wants the corn and peas in separate dishes _____

6. A person who keeps checking a clock when waiting for a bus _____

APPLY *Read each statement. Write a response using the word in* **boldface.**

7. Think about a time you felt **impatient**. What made you feel impatient?

_____

8. At what time of day do you feel most **energetic**? Why do you think this is so?

_____

9. Some people are **finicky** about what they eat. What are you finicky about?

_____

10. Do you think a cook should be **resourceful**? Explain your answer.

_____

Introducing the Words

Read the following contemporary fiction passage about a young athlete. Notice how the highlighted words are used. These are the words you will be learning in this unit.

The Competitive Edge
(Contemporary Fiction)

My friend Denise was the best distance runner on our track team. At least, I always assumed she was. In spring, we both run in 3-kilometer races in the vicinity of our school. She comes in first, and I might come in fifth or so—on a good day. I'm just not that focused on winning, I guess, and I certainly never thought anyone would displace Denise as the team's top runner.

"Maya, you have to be more competitive!" Coach Karen told me after my last race. "Today, you looked like you were jogging downtown for an ice cream cone."

Coach isn't always considerate of my feelings. Still, there's truth to what she says. If you took a poll, most people would say athletes are naturally competitive, but for some reason, I wasn't. Not that there's anything bad or improper about wanting to win—especially in sports. In fact, a competitive spirit is a healthy thing. So why didn't I have more of it?

That's what was on my mind last Friday just before the 3-kilometer race in Gray Falls. When the race began, I watched Denise jump out to the lead as I fell back to the middle of the pack.

This was identical to what had happened at the beginning of my last two races. I had come in sixth and seventh in those, but suddenly, that wasn't good enough. All of a sudden, I felt like winning!

We were already running at a brisk pace, but I picked it up a bit. Running hard, I moved ahead of the two girls in front of me. This was risky because pacing is all-important in distance running. If I wasn't careful, I might not have enough energy to finish. I might come in last and humiliate myself.

One thing was obvious. I wasn't jogging for ice cream today. In fact, I was gaining on Denise. With each step, I saw the soles of her track shoes more clearly. Usually, my mind races faster than my body does in a race. I think about how far I've run and how far I have to go. I estimate how much energy I have left. I second-guess every move I make. This race, however, was different. This time, my mind was completely empty except for one thought: I'm going to pull ahead!

Incredibly enough, I did. I crossed the finish line less than a meter ahead of Denise. I had won my first race!

"Good race!" I said to Denise after we had caught our breaths.

"Yeah," she muttered, looking like she was in shock after her unexpected downfall.

"Lucky win for me," I heard myself say. I guess I came up with that to soothe Denise's feelings.

Just then, Coach came over. "That was more than luck," she said. "You both ran a great race. It's just that Maya wanted the win more—finally!"

I have to admit that winning the race felt great. It's a memory I cherish. Also, now that I've won once, I want to prove that I can do it again. Maybe that's what competition is all about.

Definitions

You were introduced to the words below in the passage on pages 88–89. Study the pronunciation, spelling, part of speech, and definition of each word. Write the word in the blank space in the sentence that follows. Then read the synonyms and antonyms.

1. brisk
(brisk)

(adj.) energetic, lively, fast; cool and fresh
The flag snapped and fluttered in the

_____ *wind.*

SYNONYMS: quick, active, peppy; refreshing, nippy
ANTONYMS: slow, dull, sluggish

2. cherish
(cher' ish)

(v.) to feel or show great love for; to value highly; to take special care of
Our freedom is something we should always safeguard and

_____.

SYNONYMS: to treasure, hold dear, honor; to prize, preserve
ANTONYMS: to hate, despise, dishonor; to neglect

3. considerate
(kən si' də rət)

(adj.) showing concern for the needs or feelings of others
If you are a _____ *guest, you might be invited back.*

SYNONYMS: thoughtful, kind, giving, gracious
ANTONYMS: thoughtless, self-centered, selfish

4. displace
(dis plās')

(v.) to force to move or flee; to move out of position
Officials feared that the flood would

_____ *the villagers from their homes.*

SYNONYMS: to uproot, expel, evict, dislodge
ANTONYMS: to settle, plant, install

5. downfall
(daùn' fôl)

(n.) a sudden fall from power or position; a sudden, heavy snow or rain
To this day, historians argue over what caused the Roman empire's

_____.

SYNONYMS: collapse, ruin
ANTONYMS: triumph, success

6. estimate
(v., es' tə māt;
n., es' tə mət)

(v.) to form a rough judgment about size, quantity, or value
I would _____ *the number of people at the concert at about 15,000.*

(n.) a rough calculation; a careful guess

The mechanic gave us an _____ for the auto repairs.

SYNONYMS: (v.) to figure, judge; (n.) a calculation, opinion

---

7. humiliate
(hyü mi' lē āt)

(v.) to hurt someone's self-respect or pride

Our opponents accused us of trying to _____ them by running up the score.

SYNONYMS: to shame, disgrace, dishonor, embarrass
ANTONYMS: to honor, applaud, praise

---

8. identical
(ī den' ti kəl)

(adj.) exactly the same, alike in every way

The twins liked to wear _____ outfits.

SYNONYM: matching
ANTONYMS: unlike, different, opposite

---

9. improper
(im prä' pər)

(adj.) not correct; showing bad manners or taste

The principal reminded us that _____ behavior is not acceptable.

SYNONYMS: incorrect, wrong; impolite, unsuitable, rude
ANTONYMS: proper, right; appropriate, polite

---

10. poll
(pōl)

(n.) a collecting of votes; (usually plural) a place where voting takes place; a collecting of opinions

Where did you see the results of the _____?

(v.) to receive votes; to vote; to question people to collect opinions

We are going to _____ our classmates about their favorite movies.

SYNONYMS: (n.) an election; a survey, tally; (v.) to interview, tally up

---

11. soothe
(süth)

(v.) to make calm; to ease pain or sorrow

A nurse tried to _____ the fussy child.

SYNONYMS: to quiet, pacify; to comfort, relieve
ANTONYMS: to excite, upset; to hurt, worsen

---

12. vicinity
(və si' nə tē)

(n.) the area near a place, the surrounding region

There is a park in the _____ of our school.

SYNONYMS: neighborhood, area, surroundings

Match the Meaning

 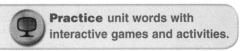
For each item below, choose the word whose meaning is suggested by the clue given. Then write the word in the space provided.

1. Things that look exactly alike are said to be _____.
   a. brisk   b. improper   c. identical   d. considerate

2. A heavy snowstorm would produce a(n) _____.
   a. estimate   b. poll   c. vicinity   d. downfall

3. To make an injury less painful is to _____ it.
   a. soothe   b. humiliate   c. displace   d. cherish

4. A grocery store in your neighborhood is in the _____ of your home.
   a. poll   b. vicinity   c. downfall   d. estimate

5. A cool, breezy morning might be described as _____.
   a. considerate   b. identical   c. improper   d. brisk

6. A person who is thoughtful of the feelings of others is said to be

   _____.

   a. considerate   b. improper   c. identical   d. brisk

7. To learn the opinions of consumers, you might _____ them.
   a. cherish   b. poll   c. displace   d. estimate

8. To take special care of something is to _____ it.
   a. poll   b. estimate   c. displace   d. cherish

9. A rough calculation is also called a(n) _____.
   a. vicinity   b. downfall   c. estimate   d. poll

10. To move something aside is to _____ it.
   a. estimate   b. displace   c. soothe   d. humiliate

11. Rude behavior might be criticized as _____.
   a. brisk   b. improper   c. considerate   d. identical

12. To embarrass or disgrace someone is to _____ that person.
   a. poll   b. soothe   c. cherish   d. humiliate

Parents often sing lullabies to **soothe** a baby at bedtime.

Synonyms

*For each item below, choose the word that is most nearly the **same** in meaning as the word or phrase in **boldface**. Then write your choice on the line provided.*

1. dislodged by the earthquake
a. cherished   b. displaced   c. polled   d. soothed   _____

2. embarrassed by a failing grade
a. cherished   b. soothed   c. humiliated   d. displaced   _____

3. treasure the memory of my first home run
a. estimate   b. poll   c. cherish   d. humiliate   _____

4. survey voters on their choice for senator
a. humiliate   b. estimate   c. poll   d. soothe   _____

5. recommended a restaurant in the **area**
a. downfall   b. vicinity   c. poll   d. estimate   _____

6. judged the distance to be thirty feet
a. polled   b. estimated   c. cherished   d. humiliated   _____

Antonyms

*For each item below, choose the word that is most nearly **opposite** in meaning to the word or phrase in **boldface**. Then write your choice on the line provided.*

1. the general's **triumph**
a. downfall   b. estimate   c. poll   d. vicinity   _____

2. set a **slow** pace
a. identical   b. brisk   c. improper   d. considerate   _____

3. held **different** views
a. improper   b. brisk   c. identical   d. considerate   _____

4. truly **thoughtless** behavior
a. considerate   b. brisk   c. identical   d. improper   _____

5. worsened the pain
a. humiliated   b. estimated   c. polled   d. soothed   _____

6. correct use of the word
a. brisk   b. considerate   c. improper   d. identical   _____

Completing the Sentence

Choose the word from the box that best completes each item below. Then write the word in the space provided. (You may have to change the word's ending.)

brisk	cherish	considerate
displace	downfall	estimate
humiliate	identical	improper
poll	soothe	vicinity

A Political Charge Backfires

■ In a heated speech late in the campaign, the mayor's opponent accused her of the _____ use of public funds. The mayor immediately denied the charge, declaring that she had never personally profited from her office.

■ A local newspaper conducted a _____ of likely voters. The results showed that more than 75% of those surveyed did not believe the charge leveled against the mayor.

■ Rather than be _____ by what would almost certainly be a lopsided defeat, her opponent pulled out of the race. The mayor went on to win by a landslide.

The Buffalo Trail

■ Before they were forcibly _____ by federal troops and European settlers, hundreds of thousands of Native Americans dwelled on the Great Plains.

■ _____ autumn winds and deep winter snows made warm clothing and shelter essential to survival on the Great Plains. Some of these robes and the tents were made from buffalo hides.

■ Because they were so dependent upon the buffalo for food as well, many tribes never strayed very far from the _____ of the huge herds that grazed the prairie.

■ Experts _____ that as many as 30 million buffalo once roamed the vast open stretches of the northern Plains.

■ The Great Plains tribes _____ their traditions and way of life. To dishonor these customs was a serious offense.

■ The destruction of the buffalo herds in the late 1800s was one of the factors that led to the _____ of these tribes.

A Friend's Good Turn

■ I was very upset to learn that a friend planned to come to the party in a costume _____ to mine.

■ To _____ my hurt feelings, she offered to wear a different costume.

■ It was very _____ of her to do that for me, don't you think?

Word Study • Context Clues 2

The **context clues** in a sentence or in surrounding sentences can help you figure out the meaning of an unfamiliar word. Here are three more types of context clues. Notice the words that signal each type of clue.

Cause/Effect	In a cause and effect statement, an unfamiliar word may appear in either the cause or effect part of the statement. The familiar words in one part help to explain the unfamiliar word in the other part. *A mouse can squeeze through a crack because its bones are **flexible**.* Signal words: *because, since, so, as a result*
Contrast	An antonym or a phrase meaning "the opposite of" explains the meaning of the unfamiliar word. *I thought the audition went well, but the results turned out to be **dismal**.* Signal words: *however, although, nevertheless, unlike, but*
Comparison	A word or phrase having the same or similar meaning as an unfamiliar word explains the meaning of the unfamiliar word. *The **dank** cellar is chilly and damp. Moreover, it is dark and musty.* Signal words: *similarly, in addition, moreover*

PRACTICE *Read each sentence. Write the meaning of the **boldface** word. Underline the words that helped you figure out its meaning.*

1. An African elephant's ears are enormous. In addition, its body is **massive**.

_____

2. Although most members of the cat family dislike the water, tigers seem to **savor** a swim on a hot day. _____

3. A tarantula is a large, hairy spider that looks dangerous. As a result, some people have a false **impression** that the spider's bite is poisonous. _____

APPLY *Complete each sentence to show you understand the meaning of the word in **boldface**. Be sure the signal word makes sense in your sentence.*

4. Since I made a good **impression** on my teacher, he _____.

5. I **savor** my meals with Dad. In addition, I _____.

6. I was prepared for the **massive** storm. However, _____.

Speak *With a partner, look through books or magazines to find sentences with signal words. Discuss the kinds of context clues that are in those sentences.*

Vocabulary for Comprehension

Read the following passage in which some of the words you have studied in Units 7–9 appear in **boldface.** *Then answer the questions on page 97.*

America's First Female Doctor

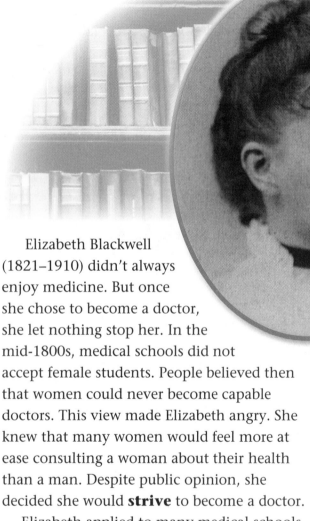

Elizabeth Blackwell (1821–1910) didn't always enjoy medicine. But once she chose to become a doctor, she let nothing stop her. In the mid-1800s, medical schools did not accept female students. People believed then that women could never become capable doctors. This view made Elizabeth angry. She knew that many women would feel more at ease consulting a woman about their health than a man. Despite public opinion, she decided she would **strive** to become a doctor.

Elizabeth applied to many medical schools, but she was rejected by each and every one. Refusing to be discouraged, Elizabeth made **alternate** plans for her education. She read thick medical textbooks on her own. She convinced an understanding doctor to be her private tutor. She never stopped working, and she never gave up hope.

Finally, in 1847, a small college in upstate New York admitted Elizabeth into its medical program. When she got there, she learned that her acceptance was a joke. Some teachers and classmates tried to **humiliate** her. Others ignored her. But Elizabeth did not let such **improper** behavior keep her from accomplishing her goal. An **industrious** student, she went to her classes and studied hard. Eventually, she earned the admiration of her fellow students.

In January 1849, Elizabeth Blackwell graduated at the head of her class. She became the first woman in the United States to receive a medical degree. At her graduation, she said, "It shall be the effort of my life to shed honor on this diploma." In so doing, she broke down the **barriers** that prevented women from practicing medicine.

Fill in the circle next to the choice that best completes the sentence or answers the question.

1. In this passage, the meaning of **strive** is
   - (a) give up.
   - (b) work slowly.
   - (c) change.
   - (d) try hard.

2. The meaning of **alternate** in this passage is
   - (a) take turns.
   - (b) peculiar.
   - (c) other.
   - (d) enormous.

3. Another word for **humiliate** is
   - (a) encourage.
   - (b) embarrass.
   - (c) assist.
   - (d) prevent.

4. Based on this passage, Elizabeth Blackwell can best be described as
   - (a) sensitive.
   - (b) determined.
   - (c) nervous.
   - (d) curious.

5. The meaning of **improper** in this passage is
   - (a) polite.
   - (b) helpful.
   - (c) understanding.
   - (d) rude.

6. **Industrious** most nearly means
   - (a) hard working.
   - (b) idle.
   - (c) interested.
   - (d) blunt.

7. In this passage, the meaning of **barriers** is
   - (a) wheels.
   - (b) goals.
   - (c) obstacles.
   - (d) vehicles.

8. What can be learned from Elizabeth Blackwell?
   - (a) the need for a sense of humor
   - (b) the importance of goals
   - (c) the meaning of friendship
   - (d) the value of medical research

Write Your Own

Elizabeth Blackwell accomplished a difficult goal despite many barriers. Think of a time when you worked hard to accomplish a goal. Write to tell what you accomplished and how you were able to do it. Use at least three words from Units 7–9.

Introducing the Words

Read the following textbook entry about a disaster that struck Ireland in the mid-1800s. Notice how the highlighted words are used. These are the words you will be learning in this unit.

Ireland's Great Famine
(Textbook Entry)

High in the Andes Mountains of Peru, in a climate too cold for corn, the Inca people grew the first potatoes. The Spanish who arrived in Peru in 1532 were interested in gold and silver, not potatoes. Nevertheless, when they descended the Andes and left Peru, they carried some of the strange new vegetables with them and later brought them back to

A farmer needed only a shovel to plant potatoes.

Spain. From there, the potato spread to other parts of Europe. Many people who grew and ate potatoes enjoyed the new food, but some doctors and scientists had serious doubts. They condemned potatoes, claiming they caused disease. In France, some even tried to abolish the planting of the new crop, claiming it ruined the soil. Despite these extreme reactions, however, most Europeans eventually realized that potatoes were a good source of nutrition.

Nowhere were potatoes grown more widely than in Ireland. In the 1600s, Ireland was a very poor country, controlled by an English parliament that acted like a dictator. Most Irish farmers could only afford to rent small plots of land. Raising enough food for a family was a constant challenge. The thrifty Irish farmers saw that they could grow more potatoes on their land than they could wheat, oats, or barley. Also, potato fields did not need to be plowed. As a result, a farmer did not need a horse and plow—only a shovel—to plant potatoes. For these reasons, potatoes became Ireland's main source of food.

For over a century, the new crop helped feed a growing population. Then, in 1845, disaster struck. A fungus, which is a type of plant growth, attacked the crop. On a visual level, its effects were horrifying. It could turn a healthy green potato field into a dark, wilted mess. On a practical level, the harm it could cause soon became clear as well. The fungus destroyed half of Ireland's potato crop that year. Although this occurrence caused widespread hunger, most people survived and looked forward to the next harvest. In fact, many farmers expanded their fields, hoping to grow more potatoes the following year to make up for their losses.

Sadly, the farmers' hopes were in vain. In the summer of 1846, the fungus reappeared. This time, Ireland's entire potato crop was lost. The nation's food supply chain, already fragile and brittle, snapped. Food prices shot up, and a serious famine gripped the land. To survive, people appealed to friends and relatives for help. They sold whatever portable possessions they had on hand in order to buy food. Eventually, they had nothing left that could be carried away. Even worse, after a time, there was no food left to buy.

The potato fungus was like a predator, and the Irish people were its prey. Weak from hunger, many were unable to fight off disease. To make matters worse, the normally mild Irish winter turned bitterly cold in the winter of 1846–1847. By 1848, about a million people had died of hunger or disease. Another million had left Ireland to start new lives in North America. In the years that followed, good potato harvests returned, but for the estimated one-quarter of the population that had died or emigrated, it was too late.

By 1848, about one million Irish emigrants had sailed to North America.

In 1845, a fungus destroyed much of Ireland's potato crop.

Definitions

You were introduced to the words below in the passage on pages 98–99. Study the pronunciation, spelling, part of speech, and definition of each word. Write the word in the blank space in the sentence that follows. Then read the synonyms and antonyms.

1. abolish
(ə bä′ lish)

(v.) to do away completely with something; to put an end to

Will human beings ever be able to _____ war?

SYNONYMS: to outlaw, ban, repeal, stamp out
ANTONYMS: to establish, restore

2. appeal
(ə pēl′)

(n.) a sincere or strong request for something that is needed; a quality or ability that attracts or interests people; a request to a higher court for review of a legal decision

Some people don't understand the

_____ of video games.

(v.) to ask strongly for help, understanding, or something else needed; to be attractive or interesting; to request review of a legal decision

Our class will _____ for aid for the homeless.

SYNONYMS: (n.) a plea, petition; charm, attraction; (v.) to plead, implore, beg
ANTONYMS: (v.) to repel, disgust, repulse

3. brittle
(bri′ təl)

(adj.) easily broken, snapped, or cracked; not flexible

The pages of the old book had turned _____.

SYNONYMS: breakable, stiff, unbending, fragile
ANTONYMS: bendable, flexible, elastic, rugged

4. condemn
(kən dem′)

(v.) to criticize a person or action as wrong, guilty, or evil; to judge as guilty and to punish

The judge is expected to _____ the defendant to life in prison.

SYNONYMS: to disapprove, denounce, blame
ANTONYMS: to praise, admire, honor, applaud, approve

5. descend
(di send′)

(v.) to move to a lower place from a higher one; to come or be handed down from the past

We watched the climber _____ the cliff.

SYNONYMS: to drop, fall, plunge, climb down; to stem, derive
ANTONYMS: to rise, climb, scale, ascend

6. dictator
(dik′ tā tər)

(n.) a ruler or leader who has total power
Sometimes my older brother acts like

a _____.

SYNONYMS: tyrant, master, despot, oppressor

7. expand
(ik spand′)

(v.) to open up, make or grow larger; to develop

The principal plans to _____ our classroom.

SYNONYMS: to spread, stretch, swell, enlarge
ANTONYMS: to shrink, reduce, contract, abridge

8. famine
(fa′ mən)

(n.) a severe shortage of food over a large area

Children especially suffered during the _____.

SYNONYMS: hunger, starvation, scarcity, want
ANTONYMS: feast, plenty

9. portable
(pôr′ tə bəl)

(adj.) easily moved or carried

Dad put a _____ crib in the trunk.

SYNONYMS: movable, transportable
ANTONYMS: immovable, fixed, rooted

10. prey
(prā)

(n.) an animal hunted as food by another; someone or something that is helpless against attack

The documentary showed a lion stalking its _____.

(v.) to hunt for food; to harm, rob, or take advantage of

Only a bully would _____ upon the weak.

SYNONYMS: (n.) a victim; quarry; (v.) to devour; to bully, victimize, cheat
ANTONYMS: (n.) a hunter, predator

11. thrifty
(thrif′ tē)

(adj.) careful about spending money; tending to save money; managing money well

My parents are teaching me to be a _____ shopper.

SYNONYMS: economical, frugal, tightfisted
ANTONYMS: wasteful, careless, extravagant

12. visual
(vi′ zhə wəl)

(adj.) having to do with sight or seeing
The math teacher likes to use

_____ aids.

SYNONYMS: visible, pictured, shown, illustrated

Match the Meaning

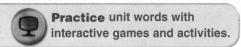

For each item below, choose the word whose meaning is suggested by the clue given. Then write the word in the space provided.

1. To judge an action as wrong is to _____ it.
   a. condemn   b. descend   c. expand   d. abolish

2. New rooms will _____ the museum's exhibit space.
   a. condemn   b. expand   c. abolish   d. descend

3. Something that is hunted is called _____.
   a. prey   b. famine   c. appeal   d. dictator

4. An object that you can pick up and carry with you could be
described as _____.
   a. brittle   b. visual   c. portable   d. thrifty

5. A serious food shortage might cause a(n) _____.
   a. prey   b. appeal   c. dictator   d. famine

6. To put an end to something is to _____ it.
   a. appeal   b. abolish   c. descend   d. expand

7. Something that attracts is said to have _____.
   a. appeal   b. prey   c. dictator   d. famine

8. A ruler who does not share power is a(n) _____.
   a. appeal   b. prey   c. dictator   d. famine

9. An object that snaps easily is said to be _____.
   a. visual   b. brittle   c. portable   d. thrifty

10. A _____ experience is one that has to do with sight
or seeing.
   a. brittle   b. portable   c. thrifty   d. visual

11. To move downward is to _____.
   a. expand   b. descend   c. abolish   d. condemn

12. A person who looks for bargains is _____.
   a. thrifty   b. portable   c. visual   d. brittle

A porcupine's sharp quills provide protection from animals that might **prey** on it.

Synonyms

*For each item below, choose the word that is most nearly the **same** in meaning as the word or phrase in **boldface**. Then write your choice on the line provided.*

1. a **movable** television

   a. brittle   b. portable   c. thrifty   d. visual   _____

2. reported on the terrible **scarcity**

   a. appeal   b. prey   c. dictator   d. famine   _____

3. a powerful and selfish **tyrant**

   a. prey   b. famine   c. appeal   d. dictator   _____

4. **plead** for help

   a. abolish   b. descend   c. appeal   d. prey   _____

5. **visible** proof of the break-in

   a. visual   b. brittle   c. thrifty   d. portable   _____

6. turned **stiff** by the cold

   a. brittle   b. visual   c. portable   d. thrifty   _____

Antonyms

*For each item below, choose the word that is most nearly **opposite** in meaning to the word or phrase in **boldface**. Then write your choice on the line provided.*

1. **shrink** the size of the project

   a. expand   b. descend   c. appeal   d. condemn   _____

2. tracked the **predator**

   a. dictator   b. prey   c. appeal   d. famine   _____

3. **restore** the tax on medicine

   a. condemn   b. descend   c. abolish   d. expand   _____

4. **praised** the decision

   a. appealed   b. descended   c. abolished   d. condemned   _____

5. a **wasteful** consumer

   a. portable   b. visual   c. thrifty   d. brittle   _____

6. **ascend** the mountain

   a. prey upon   b. descend   c. abolish   d. expand   _____

Completing the Sentence

Choose the word from the box that best completes each item below. Then write the word in the space provided. (You may have to change the word's ending.)

abolish	appeal	brittle
condemn	descend	dictator
expand	famine	portable
prey	thrifty	visual

An End to Slavery

■ Before the Civil War, many northerners _____ slavery as a terrible evil, but few wanted to go to war because of it. Abraham Lincoln, too, personally hated slavery but was prepared to accept it if by doing so the Union could be preserved.

■ Once the war began, however, many in the North argued that the time had come to

_____ slavery once and for all. In 1863 Lincoln issued the Emancipation Proclamation, freeing slaves in the states of the Confederacy.

■ Abraham Lincoln's enemies called him a(n) _____ because he exercised so much power during the war.

■ Illustrators and photographers accompanied Union troops during some of the war's

bloodiest campaigns, leaving us an important _____ record of the horrors experienced by the soldiers on both sides of the conflict.

■ Some African Americans who have _____ from slave families have passed along dramatic stories of their ancestors' experiences.

Drought Leads to Hunger

■ Without enough water, plant fibers dry out and become _____. If a drought lasts for a long time, plants and crops die.

■ If too many plants die, insects have no food, and the birds and animals that

_____ on insects then lose their food supply, too.

■ The threat of _____ can drive animals great distances in search of food.

■ If these animals do not _____ their hunting area, they too will starve.

A Teacher on a Budget

■ It would help our teacher a lot to have a laptop, a _____ computer, that she could take back and forth between school and her home.

■ She has asked businesses to donate equipment that they no longer need. So far, many

businesses have answered her _____ with computers for our classroom.

■ It has been a very _____ way of modernizing our classroom because it has cost hardly anything at all.

Word Associations

*Circle the letter next to the word or expression that best completes the sentence or answers the question. Pay special attention to the word in **boldface.***

1. A **dictator** is most likely
   a. to be loved.
   b. to be honored.
   c. to be elected.
   d. to be feared.

2. If a book **appeals** to you,
   a. you will probably read it.
   b. it is probably very long.
   c. it is probably boring.
   d. you will never read it.

3. Which would most likely be **condemned**?
   a. promptness
   b. cruelty
   c. generosity
   d. kindness

4. A **thrifty** person would
   a. give all of her money away.
   b. never buy anything on sale.
   c. count every penny.
   d. leave a generous tip.

5. If a rule is **abolished**,
   a. it must be obeyed.
   b. it is in effect only one day.
   c. it is no longer in effect.
   d. it lasts forever.

6. Which is a **visual** aid?
   a. a cane
   b. a set of false teeth
   c. a crutch
   d. a pair of glasses

7. If a **famine** struck,
   a. water would be scarce.
   b. food would be scarce.
   c. money would be scarce.
   d. gasoline would be scarce.

8. Which is a bird of **prey**?
   a. a canary
   b. a robin
   c. a hummingbird
   d. a hawk

9. Which might you **descend**?
   a. a ladder
   b. a lake
   c. a lily
   d. a lasso

10. If my waistline **expands**, I get
    a. taller.
    b. bigger around the middle.
    c. shorter.
    d. smaller around the middle.

11. If something is **brittle**,
    a. it breaks easily.
    b. it freezes quickly.
    c. it is hard to see.
    d. it is easy to carry.

12. Which type of house is meant to be **portable**?
    a. a 15-room mansion
    b. a house trailer
    c. a log cabin
    d. a schoolhouse

Word Study • Roots *port, mit*

A **root** is the main part of a word. Roots have meaning, but few roots can stand alone. Knowing the meaning of a root can sometimes help you figure out the meaning of a word. Often, the root comes from a different language, such as Latin or Greek.

port—carry
The root **port** appears in **portable** (page 101). When something is **portable**, it is easily moved or carried.
mit—send
The root **mit** appears in **emit**. When buses **emit** fumes, they give off unhealthy smoke and gases.

The chart below shows the meanings of some words with the roots *port* and *mit*.

import	to bring goods or materials into one country from another
porter	someone whose job it is to carry bags or other loads
submit	to send something in for consideration
transmit	to send out from one place or person to another; broadcast

PRACTICE *Complete each sentence with a word that contains the root* **port** *or* **mit**. *Choose from the words above.*

1. When do we have to _____ our ideas for the science fair?

2. The _____ helped us get our suitcases off the bus.

3. Many countries _____ bananas from Costa Rica.

4. Sneeze into a tissue so you don't _____ your cold.

5. Stores on an island _____ most of their merchandise.

6. The principal uses a microphone to _____ daily announcements.

APPLY *Complete each sentence to show you understand the meaning of the word in* **boldface**.

7. The hotel guest asked the **porter** to _____.

8. If I don't **submit** my application by June 15, I'll _____.

9. You can **transmit** information by _____.

10. Some things our country might **import** are _____.

Work with a partner to list other words that contain the roots **port** *and* **mit**. *Write definitions for the words. Then consult a dictionary, either in a book or online, to check the meanings.*

Shades of Meaning • Idioms 1

In the passage "Ireland's Great Famine" on pages 98–99, you read this sentence: *Food prices shot up, and a serious **famine** gripped the land*. In this sentence, the word *famine* means "a severe shortage of food."

An **idiom** is an expression that has a special meaning. You cannot figure out its meaning from the individual words. Here is an example: *Along the boardwalk, business is **either feast or famine**. Business is robust when the weather is sunny and warm, but it is slow when it is rainy and cold*. Here, the idiom *either feast or famine* has nothing to do with food. Instead, the expression means "either too much or too little of something."

PRACTICE *Read each sentence. Figure out the meaning of each idiom in boldface. Write the number of the sentence next to the meaning of the idiom.*

1. I was supposed to give my speech today, but I **got cold feet** and asked to be excused.

2. I worked **against the clock** to finish my book report.

3. Don't **add fuel to the fire** by criticizing how we played in the game that we lost.

4. I'm going **out on a limb** by giving her a second chance. After all, she did try hard.

_____ put yourself in a tough position to support someone

_____ make a bad situation worse than it is

_____ rushed and short on time

_____ became too nervous to go through with something

APPLY *Read each sentence. Figure out the meaning of each idiom in boldface. Write the meaning on the line provided.*

5. You have become such a **couch potato** that we can't persuade you to do anything else.

_____

6. When my best friend also made the soccer team, it was the **icing on the cake**.

_____

7. While I was waiting to hear the test results, I was **on pins and needles**.

_____

8. Don't **spill the beans** about the party. It's a surprise.

_____

Introducing the Words

Read the following magazine article about a daring rescue group. Notice how the highlighted words are used. These are the words you will be learning in this unit.

National Ski Patrol to the Rescue
(Magazine Article)

Avalanche! Without warning it happens. A mountainside of loose snow suddenly slides down a slope toward a downhill skier. As the skier looks up in horror, he loses his footing. It is as if a carpet has suddenly been pulled out from under his feet. Tons of snow knock him over and drag him down the hillside.

In seconds, the skier is buried. At first, he is angry with himself for not staying with his group and for getting himself into such a dangerous situation. Muttering tart comments about his bad luck, he tries to dig his way to the surface. He is too deeply buried for that, though. Instead, he decides to stay still and conserve the oxygen in the air pockets around him. Absurd as it sounds, the skier nestles into the snow, hoping that other members of his ski party will have seen the avalanche and notice that he is missing.

Fortunately, the buried skier is wearing a beacon. This electronic device sends out a regular signal to help rescuers locate him. There is no realistic way to avoid all the dangers of winter in the backcountry. Devices like beacons, however, reduce a skier's risk in the wilderness.

The skier's companions have seen the avalanche and realize that their partner is missing. As they race closer, they call in an urgent plea for help. Fortunately, members of the National Ski Patrol (NSP) are in the area. On snowmobiles, they navigate across the rugged landscape toward the disaster site.

Rescuers use beacons and poles to search for a skier under snow.

The National Ski Patrol is the largest winter rescue organization in the world. Since 1938, NSP volunteers have searched for and rescued thousands of skiers and hikers. The organization provides a sense of security for people who use the slopes. The guiding principle of the National Ski Patrol is to promote safe skiing and winter sports.

The National Ski Patrol classifies the country into different geographic regions. Volunteers patrol the ski slopes and wilderness ski areas in the region where they live. When choosing its volunteers, the organization is very selective. In addition to being in excellent physical shape, members must complete advanced training in outdoor emergency care. In areas where avalanches tend to occur, members receive special avalanche training, too. These steps help to ensure the success of rescue efforts.

Thanks to their high level of preparation, the NSP rescuers are able to help the skier buried by the avalanche. Immediately after arriving on the scene, they turn their own beacons to *Receive*. That lets them hear the signal from the skier's beacon. The rescuers also spot the ski mitten that the skier lost in the avalanche. That's another clue to his whereabouts.

The rescuers have identified the general area where the skier must be. Now they carefully probe the most likely areas with long aluminum poles. Methodically, they cover the area, probing every foot or so. Suddenly, they hear a muffled cry.

Fortunately, the snow is light and fluffy. It contains a lot of air. That lets the rescuers move it away quickly to reach the skier. More important, the buried man had enough air to breathe.

Soon a helicopter arrives to transport the skier to a hospital. It was a close call, but thanks to the National Ski Patrol, there was a happy ending!

Definitions

You were introduced to the words below in the passage on pages 108–109. Study the pronunciation, spelling, part of speech, and definition of each word. Write the word in the blank space in the sentence that follows. Then read the synonyms and antonyms.

1. absurd
(əb sûrd′)

(adj.) making no sense at all, going completely against or having no reason

No one is going to believe such an

_____ *story!*

SYNONYMS: silly, ridiculous, foolish, crazy, insane
ANTONYMS: sensible, wise, intelligent, sound

2. avalanche
(a′ və lanch)

(n.) a large mass of snow, ice, rocks, or other material sliding or falling swiftly down a mountainside; something resembling such an event

The skiers were almost buried by an

_____ *that came roaring down the slope.*

SYNONYMS: a landslide, flood, cascade

3. classify
(kla′ sə fī)

(v.) to group or label in an organized way

Libraries _____ *books by title, author, and subject.*

SYNONYMS: to order, arrange, sort, catalog, pigeonhole

4. ensure
(en shûr′)

(v.) to make sure, safe, or certain; to guarantee

The playground was designed to _____ *the children's safety.*

SYNONYMS: to confirm, insure
ANTONYMS: to risk, endanger

5. navigate
(na′ və gāt)

(v.) to plan and steer the course of a vessel or vehicle; to make one's way, get around

A pilot uses charts and instruments to

_____ *a helicopter.*

SYNONYMS: to guide, pilot, operate

6. nestle
(ne′ səl)

(v.) to settle down comfortably; to hold lovingly

The child likes to _____ in her grandmother's lap.

SYNONYMS: to cuddle, snuggle

7. plea
(plē)

(n.) an urgent request for help; the answer given in a law court by a person accused of a crime

The judge accepted the defendant's

_____ of not guilty.

SYNONYMS: an appeal, cry, petition, prayer

8. principle
(prin′ sə pəl)

(n.) a basic rule or law on which others are based; a belief used to tell right from wrong

A judge must be a person of high _____.

SYNONYMS: a standard, truth, guide, guideline, creed

9. realistic
(rē ə lis′ tik)

(adj.) using facts and good sense to evaluate people, things, or situations; concerned with the practical; resembling real life

The painting was so _____ that it looked like a photograph.

SYNONYMS: achievable, reasonable, sensible; true-to-life
ANTONYMS: impractical, dreamy, unrealistic, pie-in-the-sky

10. security
(si kyu̇r′ ə tē)

(n.) freedom from danger, fear, or doubt; safety

There is always heavy _____ around the White House.

SYNONYMS: protection, safekeeping, confidence, assurance
ANTONYMS: doubt, insecurity, peril

11. selective
(sə lek′ tiv)

(adj.) very careful about choosing or using

It pays to be a very _____ shopper.

SYNONYMS: choosy, particular, picky, fussy, discriminating
ANTONYMS: unselective, careless

12. tart
(tärt)

(adj.) having a sharp or sour taste; sharp in manner or tone

My sister replied with a very _____ remark.

(n.) a small pie, usually filled with fruit

I had a peach _____ for dessert.

SYNONYMS: (adj.) tangy, acid; biting, cutting, harsh; (n.) a pastry
ANTONYMS: (adj.) sweet; mild, gentle

Match the Meaning

vocabularyworkshop.com

Practice unit words with interactive games and activities.

For each item below, choose the word whose meaning is suggested by the clue given. Then write the word in the space provided.

1. To cuddle up with something is to _____.
   a. nestle   b. navigate   c. ensure   d. classify

2. If you make sure of something, you _____ it.
   a. nestle   b. ensure   c. classify   d. navigate

3. A person of high _____ will always try to do good.
   a. avalanches   b. securities   c. pleas   d. principles

4. A fussy cat will be _____ about what it eats.
   a. tart   b. realistic   c. selective   d. absurd

5. Freedom from fear leads to a sense of _____.
   a. principle   b. plea   c. avalanche   d. security

6. To decide how to label an item is to _____ it.
   a. ensure   b. classify   c. navigate   d. nestle

7. An urgent appeal is a(n) _____ for help.
   a. plea   b. security   c. avalanche   d. principle

8. Snow tumbling down a mountain is called a(n)
   _____.
   a. plea   b. principle   c. avalanche   d. security

9. A statement that makes no sense is _____.
   a. tart   b. absurd   c. selective   d. realistic

10. If you judge a school on facts and evidence, you will probably get a(n)
    _____ sense of the place.
    a. absurd   b. selective   c. tart   d. realistic

11. To steer around obstacles is to _____ safely.
    a. ensure   b. navigate   c. classify   d. nestle

12. An unripe apple can have a(n) _____ flavor.
    a. tart   b. selective   c. realistic   d. absurd

Lemonade without sugar tastes **tart**.

Synonyms

*For each item below, choose the word that is most nearly the **same** in meaning as the word or phrase in **boldface**. Then write your choice on the line provided.*

1. questioned our **standards**
   a. principles   b. securities   c. pleas   d. avalanches   _____

2. a **landslide** of mail at holiday time
   a. plea   b. security   c. principle   d. avalanche   _____

3. **appeals** to save the rain forest
   a. principles   b. avalanches   c. pleas   d. securities   _____

4. **sort** the blocks by shape and color
   a. navigate   b. ensure   c. nestle   d. classify   _____

5. **cuddle** in my mother's arms
   a. classify   b. nestle   c. ensure   d. navigate   _____

6. **pilot** a tanker through the canal
   a. ensure   b. navigate   c. classify   d. nestle   _____

Antonyms

*For each item below, choose the word that is most nearly **opposite** in meaning to the word or phrase in **boldface**. Then write your choice on the line provided.*

1. to **deny** safe passage
   a. ensure   b. classify   c. navigate   d. nestle   _____

2. a **sound** excuse for being absent
   a. tart   b. absurd   c. realistic   d. selective   _____

3. show very **careless** taste
   a. selective   b. realistic   c. absurd   d. tart   _____

4. an **impractical** view of the situation
   a. absurd   b. realistic   c. selective   d. tart   _____

5. prefer **sweet** apples
   a. selective   b. realistic   c. tart   d. absurd   _____

6. felt a sense of **danger**
   a. avalanche   b. security   c. plea   d. principle   _____

Completing the Sentence

Choose the word from the box that best completes each item below. Then write the word in the space provided. (You may have to change the word's ending.)

absurd	avalanche	classify
ensure	navigate	nestle
plea	principle	realistic
security	selective	tart

A Dog's Life

■ Some dogs are grouped by breed or by the work that they do. Highly trained dogs that work to help people are _____ as assistance dogs.

■ Handlers of these animals have to be very _____ in choosing dogs for the demanding training. Some animals are simply not suited to the work.

■ Some dogs, such as police or guard dogs, offer _____ from crime or trespassers, helping their owners feel safer in their homes.

■ Rescue dogs can go where humans can not or dare not go. For example, these dogs can safely _____ the ruins or rubble left by earthquakes or accidents, in search of survivors.

■ Large, strong dogs with thick fur, such as St. Bernards or huskies, are trained to rescue skiers or climbers trapped by _____.

■ Schools for these remarkable dogs make yearly _____ for money and for volunteers who will help prepare puppies for "canine careers."

Clowning Around

■ Like other schools, the Ringling Brothers Clown College is guided by a philosophy of education. At the Clown College, the first and foremost _____ is that just about anyone can be taught the art of clowning.

■ To _____ success as clowns, students must work hard to master many skills, including juggling, acrobatics, makeup design, and comedy writing.

■ Great clowns make sensible, ordinary tasks, like opening a box, somehow seem _____ and wacky.

■ Sarcastic clowns use insults and _____ comments to get laughs. Occasionally they make fun of people in the audience, but they usually play jokes on themselves.

■ In one funny routine, a clown dressed as a porcupine _____ against a cactus and called it "Mama."

■ The cactus looked quite _____ and lifelike from a distance, but on closer inspection it proved to be made of rubber.

Word Associations

*Circle the letter next to the word or expression that best completes the sentence or answers the question. Pay special attention to the word in **boldface**.*

1. Which would be an **absurd** gift for a two-year-old?
   a. a toy drum
   b. a beach ball
   c. a dinosaur puppet
   d. a real sports car

2. Where might you see an **avalanche**?
   a. on the ocean
   b. in the mountains
   c. in a desert
   d. in a suburb

3. You *cannot* be **classified** as
   a. a mammal.
   b. a student.
   c. a human being.
   d. a plant.

4. Which is a **plea**?
   a. "Thank you!"
   b. "That's an order!"
   c. "I forgot my lunch."
   d. "Not guilty, your honor."

5. Athletes with strong **principles**
   a. play by the rules.
   b. fight with the coach.
   c. hold out for more money.
   d. skip practice.

6. Studying hard will help **ensure**
   a. good manners.
   b. good looks.
   c. good weather.
   d. good grades.

7. Which will probably be **tart**?
   a. honey
   b. butterscotch pudding
   c. lemon juice
   d. blueberry pie

8. If a kitten **nestles**
   a. it scratches and howls.
   b. it cuddles and purrs.
   c. it chases a mouse.
   d. it laps up milk.

9. A movie about a **realistic** situation might be titled
   a. "I Married an Alligator!"
   b. "The Magic Eggplant."
   c. "Forest Fire!"
   d. "Martian Dance Party."

10. A sense of **security** makes you feel
   a. upset.
   b. nervous.
   c. safe.
   d. lucky.

11. A **selective** person might be called
   a. "Pokey Polly."
   b. "Picky Peter."
   c. "Wacky William."
   d. "Forgetful Fran."

12. Which is easiest to **navigate**?
   a. a bicycle
   b. a hot air balloon
   c. a bucking bronco
   d. a sailboat

Word Study • Homophones

Homophones are words that sound alike, but have different spellings and meanings. For example, *principle* (page 111) and *principal* are homophones. A *principle* is a basic rule or law or a belief used to tell right from wrong. A *principal* is the head of a school or organization. *Principal* means "most important." Read this sentence: *The **principal** of our school believes in the **principle** of good sportsmanship.* Notice how the sentence illustrates two different meanings of the homophones.

Look at the chart to find the spellings and meanings of other homophones.

coarse	*(adj.)* rough in texture
course	*(n.)* a route followed by something
bolder	*(adj.)* braver than someone else
boulder	*(n.)* a large rock
hoard	*(v.)* to gather things and hide them away
horde	*(n.)* a large group of people

PRACTICE *Underline the homophone that completes each sentence.*

1. The marathon runner finished the **(coarse, course)** in record time.

2. The man jumping off the high diving board is **(bolder, boulder)** than I am.

3. There was a **(hoard, horde)** of people around the famous movie star.

4. The **(bolder, boulder)** on the hiking trail was blocking our path.

5. Pigs have **(coarse, course)** hair that is sometimes used in hairbrushes.

6. I **(hoard, horde)** my allowance money in a box under my bed.

APPLY *Write a sentence using each homophone pair. Be sure to give the correct context for each word.*

7. **bolder, boulder** _____

8. **hoard, horde** _____

9. **coarse, course** _____

 Make up a riddle for one of the words in the homophone pairs below. Ask a partner to guess the word and spell it.

root/route   **pole/poll**

Example: I am the part of the plant that takes in food and water. What am I? (a root)

Shades of Meaning • Word Choice

request, plea, demand, interrogation

In the passage "National Ski Patrol to the Rescue" on pages 108–109, you read this sentence: *As they race closer, they call in an urgent* **plea** *for help*. The word *plea* is very specific. It tells you that the skiers are frightened and desperate for help. They are asking for help in an emotional way.

Words may have similar meanings, but no two words have exactly the same meaning. The words below all involve asking for something. Notice how they differ in meaning.

request	When you make a **request**, you ask for something politely or formally.
demand	A **demand** is more forceful than a request. When you make a demand, you speak in a firm way, as though you have a right to what you are asking for.
plea	A **plea** is an urgent call for help. You might make a plea if you are in a desperate, frightening, or intense situation.
interrogation	When a person conducts an **interrogation**, he or she asks questions of someone, sometimes for a long time, to get as much information as possible.

PRACTICE *Write whether each statement is making a* **request***, a* **demand***, or a* **plea***, or whether it is an* **interrogation***.*

1. Give me the money you owe me, right now! _____

2. Help me! I fell and twisted my ankle! _____

3. Could you please return the book to me tomorrow? _____

4. Where were you at 10:00 P.M.? Why didn't you call? _____

APPLY *Decide how you will ask the question in each situation below. Be prepared to explain your answers.*

5. You are angry that your sister borrowed your bike without asking. Would you make a **demand** or a **request** to get your bike back? Write what you would say.

_____

6. You need your mother's permission to go to the premiere of the new movie. Would you make a **plea** or a **request** to get her to let you go? Write what you would say.

_____

Introducing the Words

Read the following science fiction passage about a brave resident of a distant planet. Notice how the highlighted words are used. These are the words you will be learning in this unit.

A Message for Norrod

(Science Fiction)

Zela had searched the dusty landscape for food all morning but found only a few shreds of wild dates and some tasteless roots. Food transports from the home planet had stopped two months earlier, and the colonists who had come to Norrod to live and work were hungry. The planet's pitiless climate—always hot and dry—made agriculture impossible. Besides, the Norrodian colonists weren't farmers, but miners who were digging up valuable minerals. The mineral transports to the home planet—along with communications—had also stopped. Colony officials had offered a few flimsy explanations for the halt, but these excuses lacked detail and were not convincing.

Zela walked back to her dome. The dwelling, in the shape of a half-sphere, was large but poorly furnished. Before she got there, she saw an unfamiliar spacecraft spinning above one of the landing pads. As it rotated, it also moved slowly downward. The strange-looking craft must be a migrant. Had it traveled from another solar system? It did not display the flag of Zela's home planet. Curious, Zela and a few other colonists approached it. A military patrol arrived but was unable to confirm the craft's identity.

"Follow the procedure for unidentified spacecraft!" Major Po barked to his soldiers. "Do not assume this craft is friendly or neutral." Some of the soldiers had turned on message devices, hoping to get a response from the spacecraft.

"If we receive no response in fifteen minutes," Major Po stated, "we will have to take action against it."

Thirteen minutes passed, and the strange spacecraft made no response. In a daze because of the tension and suspense, Zela watched and waited.

"Prepare to destroy the intruder," Major Po ordered.

"Wait!" Zela cried, springing into action and rushing forward. "For all you know, this craft may come from a friendly planet!"

A soldier grabbed Zela, shouting insults and words of abuse. "How dare a Class 3 miner interfere with Norrodian security!" he said, sneering at Zela's worn and dusty miner's suit.

Zela didn't care whether she looked presentable. She was gauging the distance to the spacecraft—about 100 meters. Breaking free from the soldier's grasp, she raced toward it. A ladder was built into the side of the craft, and Zela quickly scrambled up to the main hatch.

Behind her, Zela heard Major Po ordering his soldiers. "Raise the deflection screens!" Surely, they would not destroy the craft while she was on it. Or would they?

Now in the main hatch, Zela saw a large green light on a control panel. Instinctively, she placed her hand on it.

"Greetings to the colonists of Norrod," a loud message immediately began. The message was in Zela's language. "This is an unmanned craft from planet Earth. It comes in peace, bringing food and supplies for your survival." Then the craft's main cargo bay door opened, revealing crates of food as well as water purifiers, solar cookers, and other appliances.

Zela slowly climbed down from the craft and walked back toward the soldiers. The crowd had grown in size, and nearly everyone was cheering and thanking Zela.

"Yes, thank you, Zela," said Major Po, approaching her. "Thank you for keeping an open mind and not giving in to fear."

Definitions

Remember

A **noun** (n.) is a word that names a person, place, or thing.

A **verb** (v.) is a word or words that express action or a state of being.

An **adjective** (adj.) is a word that describes a noun or pronoun.

You were introduced to the words below in the passage on pages 118–119. Study the pronunciation, spelling, part of speech, and definition of each word. Write the word in the blank space in the sentence that follows. Then read the synonyms and antonyms.

1. abuse
(n., ə byüs';
v., ə byüz')

(n.) improper, wrong, or cruel treatment; insulting language

The _____ of power is a danger in any government.

(v.) to put to bad use; to hurt or damage by treating badly

If you _____ your privileges, they may be taken away.

SYNONYMS: (n.) misuse, mistreatment; (v.) to harm, injure; to insult
ANTONYMS: (n.) care, support; (v.) to cherish, honor, praise

2. appliance
(ə plī' əns)

(n.) a machine or tool used to do a household job

It seemed an awfully big claim for such a little _____.

SYNONYMS: a device, utensil, contraption, gadget

3. confirm
(kən fûrm')

(v.) to agree or prove that something is true; to make sure, remove any doubt

The press secretary refused to _____ the report.

SYNONYMS: to verify, support, assure; to check
ANTONYMS: to deny, disprove; to cancel

4. dåze
(dāz)

(v.) to stun or confuse

Some predators _____ their prey with a blow to the head.

(n.) a state of confusion

When I heard that I had won the prize, I walked around in a

_____.

SYNONYMS: (v.) to numb, shock, astound, baffle, bewilder; (n.) a trance, stupor

5. flimsy
(flim' zē)

(adj.) not strong or solid; poorly made; not convincing

I don't think my teacher believed my _____ excuse for not doing my homework.

SYNONYMS: thin, light, weak, rickety, feeble; shabby, shoddy
ANTONYMS: strong, sturdy, sound; convincing

6. gauge
(gāj)

(n.) a standard measure used to tell size, thickness, and so on; an instrument used to measure

A rain _____ measures rainfall.

(v.) to measure; to estimate

The cat seemed to _____ the distance before jumping onto the windowsill.

SYNONYMS: (n.) a scale, rule, yardstick; (v.) to judge, assess; to guess

7. migrant
(mī′ grənt)

(n.) an animal or person that moves to a different region as the seasons change; a farmworker who moves seasonally to pick different crops

We passed a field full of _____ picking berries.

SYNONYMS: a traveler, nomad, drifter

8. neutral
(nü′ trəl)

(adj.) not taking any side in a disagreement or war; lacking distinction

Switzerland remained _____ in World Wars I and II.

SYNONYMS: uninvolved, uncommitted, impartial, open-minded; indefinite, vague
ANTONYMS: involved, committed, opinionated, heated; bold

9. pitiless
(pi′ ti ləs)

(adj.) showing no sorrow or regret for another's suffering or troubles

The audience booed the _____ villain.

SYNONYMS: cold, merciless, heartless, unsparing, cruel
ANTONYMS: kindhearted, merciful, sympathetic

10. presentable
(pri zen′ tə bəl)

(adj.) fit to be seen or inspected

My parents insisted that I wear _____ clothing.

SYNONYMS: suitable, proper, respectable, passable
ANTONYMS: shabby, improper, unfit, unacceptable

11. rotate
(rō′ tāt)

(v.) to turn around a central point; to alternate

Do you know how long it takes Earth to _____ once?

SYNONYMS: to circle, twirl, spin; to change, switch

12. shred
(shred)

(n.) a thin strip; a tiny piece or amount

Not a _____ of evidence was found.

(v.) to cut or tear into thin strips or small pieces; to rip up

The aide will_____ the company's old files.

SYNONYMS: (n.) a scrap, tatter, bit, fragment
ANTONYMS: (n.) a whole; (v.) to fix, mend, repair

Match the Meaning

vocabularyworkshop.com **Practice** unit words with interactive games and activities.

For each item below, choose the word whose meaning is suggested by the clue given. Then write the word in the space provided.

1. To use something in a way that brings harm to yourself or others is to

_____ it.
   a. gauge   b. rotate   c. daze   d. abuse

2. If you have been stunned, you might be in a(n) _____.
   a. gauge   b. daze   c. appliance   d. shred

3. To tear something to pieces is to _____ it.
   a. abuse   b. daze   c. shred   d. rotate

4. A _____ foe would not show mercy.
   a. flimsy   b. presentable   c. pitiless   d. neutral

5. Not to take sides is to remain _____.
   a. pitiless   b. presentable   c. flimsy   d. neutral

6. To prove something is to _____ it.
   a. daze   b. confirm   c. rotate   d. gauge

7. People or animals that move to different regions as the seasons

change are called _____.
   a. migrants   b. gauges   c. appliances   d. shreds

8. Blenders and can openers are kitchen _____.
   a. migrants   b. shreds   c. appliances   d. gauges

9. Something poorly made is said to be _____.
   a. presentable   b. flimsy   c. pitiless   d. neutral

10. A room fit to be inspected is _____.
   a. flimsy   b. pitiless   c. neutral   d. presentable

11. To alternate chores is to _____ them.
   a. shred   b. rotate   c. abuse   d. gauge

12. You would use a _____ to measure something.
   a. gauge   b. shred   c. daze   d. migrant

The refrigerator is the largest **appliance** in most kitchens.

Synonyms

*For each item below, choose the word that is most nearly the **same** in meaning as the word or phrase in **boldface**. Then write your choice on the line provided.*

1. an electrical **device** for cleaning rugs

   a. shred   b. migrant   c. gauge   d. appliance   _____

2. left behind by the **drifters**

   a. shreds   b. abuses   c. migrants   d. gauges   _____

3. wore a **respectable** outfit for the class picture

   a. presentable   b. flimsy   c. neutral   d. pitiless   _____

4. **numbed** by the terrible news

   a. gauged   b. dazed   c. rotated   d. confirmed   _____

5. **assess** the value of the coin collection

   a. shred   b. gauge   c. abuse   d. rotate   _____

6. **twirl** the plant to face the sun

   a. confirm   b. gauge   c. daze   d. rotate   _____

Antonyms

*For each item below, choose the word that is most nearly **opposite** in meaning to the word or phrase in **boldface**. Then write your choice on the line provided.*

1. **mend** the old pillowcase

   a. shred   b. confirm   c. rotate   d. gauge   _____

2. **sturdy** shoes

   a. neutral   b. flimsy   c. presentable   d. pitiless   _____

3. reported their **kindhearted** treatment

   a. neutral   b. flimsy   c. presentable   d. pitiless   _____

4. refused to **deny** the rumor

   a. gauge   b. rotate   c. confirm   d. classify   _____

5. painted in **bold** colors

   a. flimsy   b. neutral   c. presentable   d. pitiless   _____

6. fans who **praise** the umpires

   a. rotate   b. gauge   c. abuse   d. daze   _____

Completing the Sentence

Choose the word from the box that best completes each item below. Then write the word in the space provided. (You may have to change the word's ending.)

abuse	appliance	confirm
daze	flimsy	gauge
migrant	neutral	pitiless
presentable	rotate	shred

A Toast to Toast

■ One of the most common of household _____, the electric toaster, was first introduced to American kitchens in 1910.

■ Early models toasted only one side of the bread at a time. In order to toast both sides, you had to _____ the slice of bread yourself.

■ These toasters did not have self-timers, either. If you didn't pay careful attention, your toast might not look very _____.

From Field to Field

■ It is estimated that in the U.S., there are about half a million _____ who follow the harvest each year in search of work at fruit and vegetable farms.

■ These workers are often _____ by harsh bosses who pay too little and demand too much. Working and living conditions are often unsafe and unsanitary.

■ Bending over for hours under a hot sun to harvest crops can leave these workers feeling _____ by the end of a long day in the fields.

■ The _____ sun beats down on the workers, offering no mercy.

■ Some farmworkers are so poor that they barely get enough to eat, and their old, tattered clothes hang in _____.

■ Rather than stay _____ about the problems that seasonal farmworkers face, activists are taking up their cause by fighting for improved legal and civil rights.

Running on Empty

■ When our car came sputtering to a stop on a dark and lonely country road, I was almost afraid to look at the fuel _____.

■ But when I did, a quick glance was enough to _____ the worst: The car had run out of gas, just as I suspected.

■ We had to walk two miles to a gas station, with nothing more to protect us from the rain than our _____ jackets.

Word Study • Prefixes *re-, in-, im-*

You have learned that a **prefix** is a word part that is added to the beginning of a **base word** to make a new word. You can add the prefix *re-* to *confirm* (page 120) to make a new word.

The prefix **re-** usually means "again" or "back."

re + confirm = **re**confirm ⟶ means "confirm again"
re + pay = **re**pay ⟶ means "pay back"

You learned that the prefix *in-* can mean "not." The prefixes *in-* and *im-* can sometimes mean "in" or "into."

in + sight = **in**sight ⟶ means "see into"
im + migrate = **im**migrate ⟶ means "to enter into another country or area to live"

PRACTICE *Write the missing prefix and base word. Then write the meaning of the new word.*

Prefix	Base Word	New Word	Meaning
1. _____ +	_____ =	indoors ⟶	_____
2. _____ +	_____ =	refill ⟶	_____
3. _____ +	_____ =	return ⟶	_____
4. _____ +	_____ =	inborn ⟶	_____
5. _____ +	_____ =	implant ⟶	_____

APPLY *Complete each sentence with a word that contains the prefix re-, in-, or im-. Choose from the words above.*

6. My mother called to _____ the departure time of the train.

7. Our golden retriever puppy has a(n) _____ talent for fetching.

8. After my tooth got knocked out, the dentist had to _____ a fake tooth.

9. I finished reading the book, so I will _____ it to the library.

10. The scientist's research resulted in valuable _____ into ant behavior.

Watch out for words that seem to have prefixes but really do not. For example, when you remove re from ready, no base word remains. With a partner, decide which words below do not have a prefix. Underline those words. Be prepared to explain your answers.

imagine   imperfect   inhabit   ink   register   review

Vocabulary for Comprehension

*Read the following passage in which some of the words you have studied in Units 10–12 appear in **boldface**. Then answer the questions on page 127.*

Free-tailed bats emerging from caves to hunt

Census Taking

The U.S. Census Bureau takes official surveys to gather data on our population. The formal count is called a *census*. Business leaders, educators, and politicians use the data to get a **realistic** picture of the people they serve. Such groups use the information about the population to **ensure** that they understand the needs of the community.

Scientists also use census data. Can you imagine why? Scientists study plant and animal populations for many reasons. Scientists might track animal populations to learn how animals and humans can live together safely. They might study a **migrant** butterfly population to find out if the same number of butterflies returns to the same area each year. Or scientists might count the members of an endangered species in order to **appeal** for ongoing protection.

Government census workers gather data in person and by mail. But scientists must find unique ways to count the plants and animals in a given area. To estimate the population of free-tailed bats in Carlsbad Cavern, the largest cave in New Mexico, for example, scientists made use of technology. They set up video cameras outside the entrance of the cave, which houses a large number of bats. The scientists filmed the bats flying out of the cave. Later, the scientists counted the bats in each frame of the video.

Scientists sometimes just use their eyes to take a census. This **visual** method works best when the plants or animals are large in size and small in number. For example, to count the maple trees on a farm in Vermont, scientists can simply use their eyes. However, a more complex method would be needed to **gauge** the number of small animals, such as field mice, in the same vicinity.

Fill in the circle next to the choice that best completes the sentence or answers the question.

1. What is the main idea of this article?
   a) The U.S. Census Bureau gathers useful population data.
   b) Like the government, scientists gather and use census data.
   c) Carlsbad, New Mexico, is an interesting place to visit.
   d) Scientists use their eyes to count many living things.

2. The meaning of **realistic** is
   a) true-to-life.
   b) scientific.
   c) superb.
   d) strict.

3. In this passage, **ensure** means to
   a) make certain.
   b) settle down.
   c) reduce.
   d) destroy.

4. A **migrant** animal
   a) is an endangered species.
   b) has an enormous population.
   c) always stays in the same place.
   d) moves from one region to another.

5. In this passage, the meaning of **appeal** is to
   a) be attractive.
   b) ask strongly.
   c) estimate.
   d) reject.

6. **Visual** means having to do with
   a) sound or hearing.
   b) sight or seeing.
   c) feel or touching.
   d) scent or smelling.

7. In this passage, the meaning of **gauge** is
   a) a measurement tool.
   b) a certain distance.
   c) to sail a vessel.
   d) to assess.

8. Which is the most likely topic for the next paragraph of the article?
   a) when the first census was taken
   b) the number of farms in Vermont
   c) how to count small forest animals
   d) other wildlife in Carlsbad

Write Your Own

Every evening at Carlsbad Caverns in southeastern New Mexico, nearly 400,000 free-tailed bats fly out of caves in search of food. Imagine watching this stunning display of bats. On a separate sheet of paper, describe how you might feel as you watch this scene unfold. Use at least three words from Units 10–12.

Classifying

Choose the word from the box that goes best with each group of words. Write the word in the space provided. Then explain what the words have in common.

compose	famine	identical
pitiless	plea	presentable
primary	rotate	senseless
soothe	tart	verdict

1. comfort, _____, pacify, reassure

_____

2. sense, _____, sensible, sensitive

_____

3. brainstorm, outline, draft, _____

_____

4. plague, earthquake, _____

_____

5. judge, jury, _____

_____

6. _____, similar, unlike, opposite

_____

7. pity, pitiful, _____

_____

8. cookie, muffin, cake, _____

_____

9. spin, twirl, twist, _____

_____

10. glee, flea, _____, ski

_____

11. considerable, dependable, reasonable, _____

_____

12. _____, middle, secondary

_____

Completing the Idea

Complete each sentence so that it makes sense. Pay attention to the word in **boldface.**

1. I always **rejoice** when I _____.

2. An **observant** person will likely notice _____.

3. Our class took a **poll** to see _____.

4. Some animal predators catch their **prey** by _____.

5. The **security** at the museum always _____.

6. To answer the **avalanche** of questions, the speaker _____.

7. A flower may **shrivel** if _____.

8. When I feel **energetic**, I like to _____.

9. The **downfall** of the king was caused by _____.

10. Someone who is **thrifty** will _____.

11. When I am tired, I like to **nestle** _____.

12. It is best to stay **neutral** when _____.

13. In order to **enforce** the law, police officers _____.

14. The thing I **cherish** most is _____.

15. The town council voted to **abolish** _____.

16. Because I want to **expand** my vocabulary, I _____.

17. The toy was so **flimsy** that _____.

Writing Challenge

Write two sentences using the word **loot.** In the first sentence, use **loot** as a verb. In the second sentence, use **loot** as a noun.

1. _____

2. _____

Introducing the Words

Read the following passage about an early hero in the fight for American independence. Notice how the highlighted words are used. These are the words you will be learning in this unit.

Crispus Attucks Changes History

(Historical Nonfiction)

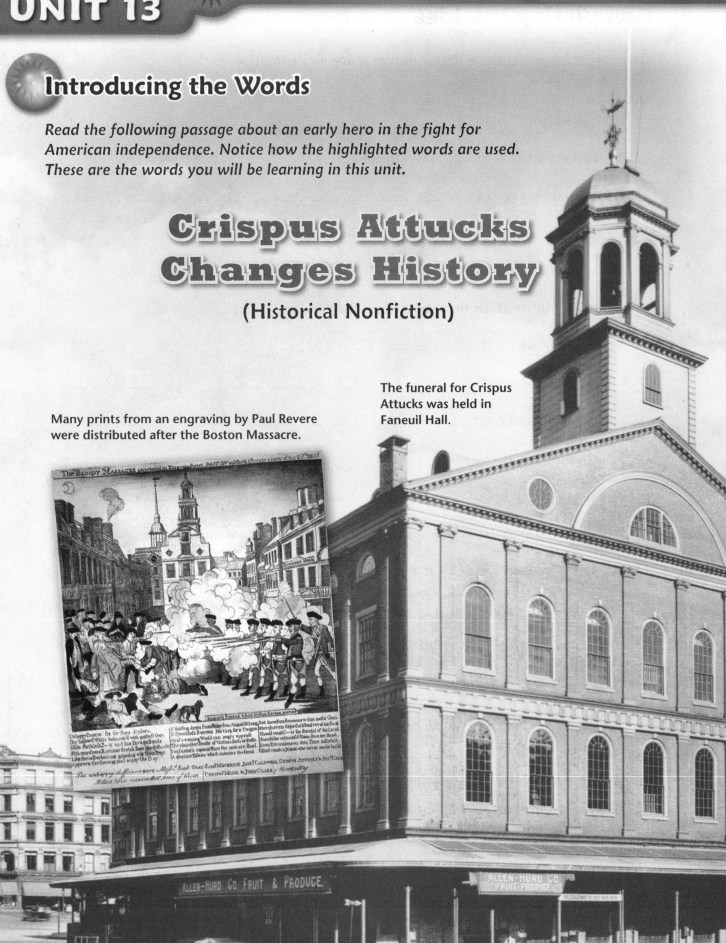

Many prints from an engraving by Paul Revere were distributed after the Boston Massacre.

The funeral for Crispus Attucks was held in Faneuil Hall.

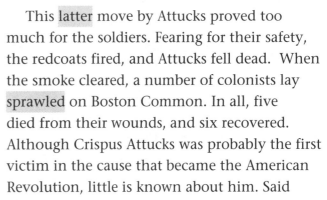

A cold wind swept in from Boston Harbor on the night of March 5, 1770, and fresh snow lay on the streets. On Boston Common, the British soldiers, who later became known as redcoats, sat inside their tents. They had been camped there for months in conditions neither comfortable nor sanitary. At a time of rising tension in the colonies, the redcoats were there to preserve the peace and enforce the new trade laws.

For the soldiers, it was a monotonous assignment; they had little to do. Sometimes, they debated political issues with the colonists. More often, the colonists hurled insults at the redcoats, whom many regarded as foes. This night, some colonists were throwing snowballs from the darkness. Accounts vary about exactly what happened next. A scuffle seems to have broken out, and a nearby church bell rang an alarm. Citizens, angry and tense about the redcoats, gathered at Boston Common. Some citizens carried sticks and clubs. As the crowd grew larger, the redcoats forced the colonists back.

Crispus Attucks

According to several accounts, a small group of colonists suddenly charged the redcoats. Urged on by their leader, a tall black man named Crispus Attucks, the men waved their simple weapons and shouted insults at the British. Attucks may have taunted the soldiers by saying, "Shoot if you dare." Then, as the crowd began to throw things at the soldiers, Attucks is said to have clubbed one of the redcoats and grabbed for his bayonet—the blade at the end of his rifle.

This latter move by Attucks proved too much for the soldiers. Fearing for their safety, the redcoats fired, and Attucks fell dead. When the smoke cleared, a number of colonists lay sprawled on Boston Common. In all, five died from their wounds, and six recovered. Although Crispus Attucks was probably the first victim in the cause that became the American Revolution, little is known about him. Said to be the son of an African father and a Native American mother, he grew up a slave in Massachusetts. In 1750, when Attucks was about 27, he ran away from his owner and may have gone to sea on a whaling ship. Nothing else was heard from him until the night of what became known as the Boston Massacre.

That's what the patriot leaders called it—a massacre—to build support for the cause of freedom. "On that night, the foundations of American independence were laid," President John Adams later wrote. Thousands of angry colonists attended a public funeral for Attucks and the other victims in Boston's Faneuil Hall. Speakers praised the bravery that Attucks had exhibited, and newspaper accounts retold the story. Attucks and the others acquired even more fame with Paul Revere's widely known engraving of the massacre. Prints made from the engraving were distributed around the colonies, building support for Boston and hatred for the redcoats.

For five years, the memory of the Boston Massacre fanned the flames of revolution. In the end, the reckless bravery of Crispus Attucks had widespread consequences. His achievement was nothing less than changing the course of American history.

Definitions

You were introduced to the words below in the passage on pages 130–131. Study the pronunciation, spelling, part of speech, and definition of each word. Write the word in the blank space in the sentence that follows. Then read the synonyms and antonyms.

1. achievement
(ə chēv′ mənt)

(n.) something done successfully; something gained by working or trying hard

A perfect report card is quite an

_____.

SYNONYMS: an accomplishment, feat, triumph
ANTONYMS: a defeat, failure, setback

2. acquire
(ə kwīr′)

(v.) to get as one's own

When did you _____ the ability to speak French so well?

SYNONYMS: to obtain, gain, earn
ANTONYMS: to lose, give up, surrender

3. debate
(di bāt′)

(n.) a discussion of reasons for and against something

The town council held a _____ on building a new library.

(v.) to discuss reasons for and against something; to think about carefully before deciding

What issue would you like to _____?

SYNONYMS: (n.) an argument, dispute; (v.) to discuss, consider
ANTONYMS: (n.) an agreement; (v.) to agree (with)

4. exhibit
(ig zi′ bət)

(v.) to show clearly; to put on display

You _____ great talent in gymnastics.

(n.) something shown to the public

We went to the diamond _____ at the science museum.

SYNONYMS: (v.) to present, reveal; (n.) a display, exhibition
ANTONYMS: (v.) to hide, conceal, cover up

5. foe
(fō)

(n.) one who hates or tries to harm another; an enemy

Identify yourself: Are you friend or _____?

SYNONYMS: an opponent, rival
ANTONYMS: a friend, ally, comrade, buddy

6. latter
(la' tər)

(adj.) closer to the end; relating to the second of two things discussed

The first part of the book is better than the _____ *part.*

SYNONYMS: last, later, end, final
ANTONYMS: former, first, earlier, beginning

7. massacre
(ma' si kər)

(n.) the cruel killing of many people or animals

The village was the site of a bloody _____.

(v.) to kill many people or animals in a cruel way

The barbarians planned to _____ *their rivals.*

SYNONYMS: (n.) a slaughter; (v.) to butcher, slaughter

8. monotonous
(mə nä' tən əs)

(adj.) dull as a result of not changing in any way

Shelling peas is a _____ *chore.*

SYNONYMS: boring, uninteresting, tiresome
ANTONYMS: varied, lively, exciting

9. preserve
(pri zûrv')

(v.) to keep safe from injury or ruin; to keep food from spoiling

I signed a petition to _____ *the wetlands.*

(n.) an area set aside for the protection of wildlife

Wild animals roam freely in the nature _____.

SYNONYMS: (v.) to save, protect, conserve; (n.) a refuge, sanctuary
ANTONYMS: (v.) to waste, destroy, misuse

10. sanitary
(sa' nə ter ē)

(adj.) having to do with health; free of dirt and germs
In a factory, the areas that produce computer parts

must remain completely _____.

SYNONYMS: clean, pure, sterile, hygienic
ANTONYMS: dirty, filthy, contaminated, unhealthy

11. sprawl
(sprôl)

(v.) to lie or sit with arms and legs spread out; to spread out in a disorderly way

Some nights I _____ *in front of the TV set.*

SYNONYMS: to lounge, slouch, relax, stretch, extend

12. widespread
(wīd' spred')

(adj.) happening in many places or to many people; fully open

Interest in the lives of movie stars is _____.

SYNONYMS: far-reaching, vast, common
ANTONYMS: limited, rare, unusual, uncommon

Match the Meaning

vocabularyworkshop.com

Practice unit words with interactive games and activities.

For each item below, choose the word whose meaning is suggested by the clue given. Then write the word in the space provided.

1. A display of paintings or other objects is a(n) _____.
   a. debate   b. preserve   c. massacre   d. exhibit

2. A belief that is held by many people is _____.
   a. latter   b. monotonous   c. widespread   d. sanitary

3. When you buy property, you _____ it.
   a. massacre   b. sprawl   c. debate   d. acquire

4. People who hate one another are _____.
   a. achievements b. foes   c. debates   d. exhibits

5. The cruel killing of many innocent people is a(n)

   _____.

   a. massacre   b. exhibit   c. achievement d. foe

6. Something that is free of germs is _____.
   a. widespread   b. monotonous   c. latter   d. sanitary

7. To consider the pros and cons of an issue is to

   _____ it.

   a. debate   b. exhibit   c. preserve   d. acquire

8. A bird sanctuary is an example of a wildlife

   _____.

   a. debate   b. massacre   c. preserve   d. foe

9. The second of two events is the _____ one.
   a. monotonous   b. latter   c. sanitary   d. widespread

10. Landing on the moon is an example of a monumental _____.
   a. preserve   b. achievement c. massacre   d. foe

11. Something that is done over and over in the same way is _____.
   a. latter   b. widespread   c. sanitary   d. monotonous

12. To lie on the floor with your arms and legs spread out is to _____.
   a. exhibit   b. preserve   c. sprawl   d. acquire

Some nights I **sprawl** in front of the TV set.

Synonyms

*For each item below, choose the word that is most nearly the **same** in meaning as the word or phrase in **boldface**. Then write your choice on the line provided.*

1. a worthy **opponent**
   a. preserve   b. exhibit   c. foe   d. debate   _____

2. slaughter the newborn harp seals
   a. preserve   b. exhibit   c. acquire   d. massacre   _____

3. the **boring** refrain of "tra-la-la"
   a. latter   b. sanitary   c. widespread   d. monotonous _____

4. consider going by train or by car
   a. sprawl   b. debate   c. acquire   d. massacre   _____

5. my proudest **accomplishment**
   a. preserve   b. exhibit   c. foe   d. achievement _____

6. lounge on the couch
   a. exhibit   b. preserve   c. sprawl   d. massacre   _____

Antonyms

*For each item below, choose the word that is most nearly **opposite** in meaning to the word or phrase in **boldface**. Then write your choice on the line provided.*

1. conceal your surprise
   a. exhibit   b. sprawl   c. massacre   d. preserve   _____

2. the **first** part of our vacation
   a. widespread   b. latter   c. monotonous   d. sanitary   _____

3. lose millions of dollars
   a. debate   b. sprawl   c. massacre   d. acquire   _____

4. limited appeal among children
   a. sanitary   b. monotonous   c. latter   d. widespread   _____

5. destroy the town records
   a. massacre   b. exhibit   c. preserve   d. sprawl   _____

6. found **unhealthy** living conditions
   a. latter   b. sanitary   c. widespread   d. monotonous _____

Completing the Sentence

Choose the word from the box that best completes each item below. Then write the word in the space provided. (You may have to change the word's ending.)

achievement	acquire	debate
exhibit	foe	latter
massacre	monotonous	preserve
sanitary	sprawl	widespread

You Can't Win Them All

■ The current events club had to decide whether to _____ hunters' rights or the child helmet law.

■ We chose the child helmet law, the _____ issue, because it was more relevant to students our age.

■ The members of our team gave such _____ speeches in favor of the law that the other team won, although their arguments were more emotional than fact-filled.

What Happened in Rwanda

■ In 1994 a brutal _____ took place in Rwanda, a country in Central Africa. Hundreds of thousands of people were injured or killed.

■ The major _____ were the Hutu and Tutsi peoples.

■ In overcrowded refugee camps, _____ conditions were dangerously poor. Clean water, food, and medicines were in short supply.

■ Rescue workers found entire families _____ on the ground. Many of these people were dying of starvation and disease.

"Four score and seven years ago . . ."

■ Many historians consider Abraham Lincoln's Gettysburg Address to be the greatest

_____ in public speaking this nation has produced.

■ The fame of this brief speech is so _____ that most Americans—and even many from other nations—know the opening of it by heart.

■ The Library of Congress _____ a copy of the speech, written in Lincoln's own hand. Only four other copies in his handwriting are still in existence.

■ At the library the manuscript is carefully _____ as a national historical treasure.

■ Sometimes the document travels to Pennsylvania for _____ in connection with special events at the actual site of the battle. The battlefield became a national park in 1895.

Word Associations

*Circle the letter next to the word or expression that best completes the sentence or answers the question. Pay special attention to the word in **boldface**.*

1. A cafeteria that is **sanitary** has
   a. good main dishes.
   b. overflowing trash bins.
   c. safely prepared food.
   d. high-priced lunches.

2. The **latter** part of December includes
   a. the first day of the month.
   b. the last week of the month.
   c. four Sundays.
   d. New Year's Day.

3. If my neighbor is my **foe**, we
   a. share a driveway.
   b. do not get along.
   c. live in the country.
   d. feed each other's pets.

4. Witnesses to a **massacre** probably feel
   a. horrified.
   b. cheerful.
   c. hungry.
   d. relaxed.

5. A **monotonous** speaker might
   a. win an award for public speaking.
   b. wake up the neighborhood.
   c. give speech lessons.
   d. put a listener to sleep.

6. A swimmer who is honored for his or her **achievements** might
   a. go waterskiing.
   b. get a sunburn.
   c. get a trophy.
   d. go to an aquarium.

7. Which of these has been **preserved**?
   a. apples on a tree
   b. berries on a vine
   c. fresh peach pie
   d. canned pears

8. Which might be included in an **exhibit** of students' work?
   a. paintings by famous artists
   b. science fair projects
   c. parents and teachers
   d. rulers and erasers

9. One way to **acquire** a rare stamp is to
   a. mail a letter.
   b. read a book about collecting stamps.
   c. buy one from a catalog.
   d. pay extra postage.

10. A participant in a **debate** should
    a. defend his or her point of view.
    b. try not to say anything.
    c. never argue with an opponent.
    d. join the football team.

11. Which of these is **widespread**?
    a. an opinion held by a few friends
    b. a belief that the earth is flat
    c. an interest in fruitflies
    d. a disease that infects many people

12. I might **sprawl** on the couch to
    a. relax.
    b. wake up.
    c. move furniture.
    d. exercise.

Word Study • Suffixes *-ion, -tion, -sion, -ous, -ic*

You have learned that a **suffix** is a word part that is added to the end of a **base word** to make a new word. You can add the suffix *-ion* to *exhibit* (page 132) to make a new word.

> The suffixes **-ion**, **-tion**, and **-sion** mean "the act, state, or result of."
>
> exhibit + **ion** = exhib**ition** ⟶ means "a display"
> compete + **tion** = compet**ition** ⟶ means "a contest"
> decide   + **sion** = deci**sion**   ⟶ means "something decided upon"
>
> The suffix **-ous** means "like" or "full of." The suffix **-ic** means "relating to."
> poison + **ous** = poison**ous** ⟶ means "full of poison"
> base   + **ic**   = bas**ic**   ⟶ means "related to the main point"

PRACTICE *Write the missing base word, suffix, or new word. Then write the meaning of the new word. Use a dictionary to check your answers.*

Base Word	Suffix	New Word	Meaning
1. _____ + ion	= prevention	⟶	_____
2. expand + _____	= expansion	⟶	_____
3. hazard + ous	= _____	⟶	_____
4. _____ + ic	= heroic	⟶	_____

APPLY *Complete each sentence with a word that contains the suffix -ion, -tion, -sion, -ous, or -ic. Choose from the words above.*

5. The park board made a _____ to develop an _____ of the gardening program.

6. Before the _____ began, the judges reviewed the _____ rules of the game with the players.

7. The _____ snakes were the main attraction at the _____.

8. A _____ lifeguard rescued a swimmer from the _____ waters and jagged rocks.

9. Daily exercise and a healthy diet are essential to the _____ of heart disease.

Continue the chart in **Practice.** *Work with a partner to list other words with the suffixes -ion, -tion, -sion, -ous, and -ic. Then list the base word, suffix, and meaning for each new word.*

Shades of Meaning • Word Choice

acquire, receive, purchase, borrow

In the passage "Crispus Attucks Changes History" on pages 130–131, you read the sentence: *Attucks and the others **acquired** even more fame with Paul Revere's widely known engraving of the massacre.* Here the word *acquired* means "got" or "gained."

You have learned that words may have similar meanings, but that no two words have exactly the same meaning. Look at the words in the chart. All the words involve getting or obtaining something. Notice how the meanings of the words differ.

acquire	When you **acquire** something, you get or obtain it for yourself.
receive	When you **receive** something, you get something from another person.
purchase	When you **purchase** something, you pay money to get it.
borrow	When you **borrow** something that belongs to someone else, you use it for a period of time with the person's permission.

PRACTICE *Write the word from the chart that best replaces the word* **get** *in each sentence.*

1. We were able to **get** one of our neighbor's puppies. _____

2. I can **get** my brother's ruler, but he needs it after school. _____

3. What did you **get** for your birthday? _____

4. Mom asked me to **get** milk and eggs at the store. _____

APPLY *Respond to each situation below. Answer in a complete sentence.*

5. You want to try riding a skateboard. Should you **purchase** or **borrow** a skateboard? Why?

   _____

6. You need a graduation gift for your friend. Will you **purchase** a gift or **receive** one? Explain.

   _____

7. You practice dribbling and kicking a soccer ball each day. Are you **acquiring** skills or **borrowing** them?

   _____

Introducing the Words

Read the following nonfiction narrative about a tourist attraction with an odd history. Notice how the highlighted words are used. These are the words you will be learning in this unit.

A Giant Hoax
(Nonfiction Narrative)

The well diggers on William Newell's farm in Cardiff, New York, got quite a shock one October morning in 1869. A few feet down, their shovels uncovered a ten-foot long man. The body appeared to be petrified—that is, over a very long time, it had turned to stone.

News of this singular discovery traveled fast. Was this proof that giants had once walked the earth? People from all over swarmed to see the giant fossil. Newell's relative, George Hull, spotted a money-making opportunity and charged each visitor ten cents a peek. As the crowds increased, Hull raised the price to fifty cents, the equivalent of about six dollars today.

Soon, a group of businessmen began to pursue Hull, begging him to sell them "the Cardiff Giant." Hull finally agreed to a price

The Cardiff Giant

Crowds formed to see the Giant.

of $37,000, and the stone creature was moved to Syracuse, New York. Now even more people lined up to see it.

Among the visitors were several paleontologists—scientists who study ancient remains. Their negative opinions of the Cardiff Giant revealed they were not impressed. Convinced it was not real, they labeled it a fraud. In support of these conclusions, they pointed out the rough chisel marks on the giant's body. They also noted that acids had been used to make the "fossil" look old. In short, William Newell and George Hull had some explaining to do.

When George Hull was questioned, he offered no cover story, no alibi. On the contrary, he was surprisingly frank. With the help of a confederate, an Iowa man who was a sculptor, he had carved the statue and modified its appearance with acid. The statue was shipped east by rail and then discharged with other cargo at a station near Cardiff. From there, Hull carted it to the farm of William Newell. He then buried the "giant" on the farm and waited a year before hiring workers to dig in the same spot.

Why would George Hull do such a thing? At the time of the hoax, many people believed that real-life giants had once walked the earth. Hull disagreed. Apparently, he just wanted to poke fun at this belief. When he saw how much money he could make, however, he decided to let people think the Cardiff Giant was real. A practical joke had turned into a money-making swindle.

The story should have ended there, but it didn't. At this time, P.T. Barnum reigned over the world of popular entertainment, and the great showman wanted the Cardiff Giant in his traveling circus. The owners, however, refused to rent it to Barnum, not even for $30,000 a month. In response, Barnum came up with a more economical approach. He had an exact replica made, put it in his show, and claimed it was the original one. This fraud should have led to a boycott or mutiny by Barnum's customers, but it didn't. Even more people lined up to see the counterfeit giant.

Like most sensations, the Cardiff Giant gradually faded from memory. For decades, it lay undisturbed in a barn near Syracuse. Eventually, however, it was put on exhibit at the Farmers' Museum in Cooperstown, New York. Today, visitors there still line up and pay to see the giant hoax.

Admission ticket

Definitions

You were introduced to the words below in the passage on pages 140–141. Study the pronunciation, spelling, part of speech, and definition of each word. Write the word in the blank space in the sentence that follows. Then read the synonyms and antonyms.

1. alibi
(a′ lə bī)

(n.) a claim of having been elsewhere when a crime was committed; a reason given to explain something

Can anyone confirm your _____?

SYNONYMS: an excuse, explanation, story, defense

2. confederate
(kən fe′ də rət)

(n.) a person, state, or country that joins with another for a common purpose; a partner in crime

Great Britain was a _____ *of the U.S. in World War II.*

SYNONYMS: an ally, accomplice
ANTONYMS: a foe, enemy

3. discharge
(v., dis chärj′;
n., dis′ chärj)

(v.) to let go; to unload cargo or passengers; to fire off; to give off

The cruise ship stopped in port to _____ *the tourists.*

(n.) a release or letting go; a firing off; a giving off; something given off

The army gave the soldier an honorable _____.

SYNONYMS: (v.) to release, dismiss, shoot; (n.) a dismissal
ANTONYMS: (v.) to detain, imprison; to hire, appoint; to load; to absorb

4. economical
(e kə nä′ mi kəl)

(adj.) careful about spending money or using resources

An _____ *shopper always looks for a bargain.*

SYNONYMS: thrifty, frugal, saving
ANTONYMS: extravagant, wasteful

5. frank
(fraŋk)

(adj.) honest in expressing thoughts and feelings

Don't be offended if I am _____ *with you.*

SYNONYMS: direct, blunt, straightforward, truthful
ANTONYMS: secretive, insincere, dishonest

6. modify
(mä′ də fī)

(v.) to change somewhat

You can _____ *a recipe to suit your taste.*

SYNONYMS: to adjust, alter, adapt, vary, revise

7. mutiny
(myü′ tən ē)

(n.) an open rebellion against authority

The Boston Tea Party was an act of _____.

(v.) to rebel against those in charge
The captain's cruelty led the crew to

_____.

SYNONYMS: (n.) a revolt, uprising, riot; (v.) to revolt, rise up
ANTONYMS: (n.) to support, obey

8. negative
(ne′ gə tiv)

(adj.) saying "no"; not positive or helpful; less than zero

The reply to my question was _____.

(n.) a "no" expression; a photo image that reverses light and dark areas

"I can't" is an example of a _____.

SYNONYMS: (adj.) bad, unfavorable
ANTONYMS: (adj.) positive, helpful, good, favorable

9. pursue
(pər sü′)

(v.) to chase in order to catch; to strive to achieve; to carry out

During a hunt, the dogs _____ *a hare.*

SYNONYMS: to follow, hunt, run after, aim for, work for
ANTONYMS: to run away, take off, flee, bolt

10. reign
(rān)

(n.) the power or rule of a monarch; a monarch's period of rule

England prospered under the _____ *of Queen Anne.*

(v.) to rule as a monarch; to be widespread

During the 1920s, prosperity _____.

SYNONYMS: (n.) the regime, control; (v.) to govern, command

11. singular
(siŋ′ gyə lər)

(adj.) referring to only one person or thing; out of the ordinary

The show was a _____ *success.*

SYNONYMS: exceptional, unusual
ANTONYM: plural

12. swindle
(swin′ dəl)

(v.) to cheat out of money or property

A dishonest shopkeeper tried to _____ *me.*

(n.) a scheme for cheating someone

The fraud squad uncovered the _____.

SYNONYMS: (v.) to deceive, trick, gyp, con; (n.) a scam, fraud, hoax, racket

Match the Meaning

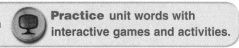

vocabularyworkshop.com   **Practice** unit words with interactive games and activities.

For each item below, choose the word whose meaning is suggested by the clue given. Then write the word in the space provided.

1. To rebel against commanding officers is to _____.
   a. discharge   b. swindle   c. modify   d. mutiny

2. To exercise the powers of a king or queen is to _____.
   a. reign   b. pursue   c. mutiny   d. modify

3. A scheme for cheating people is a _____.
   a. negative   b. discharge   c. swindle   d. confederate

4. A claim of being elsewhere during a crime is a(n) _____.
   a. alibi   b. mutiny   c. discharge   d. reign

5. When you change plans slightly, you _____ them.
   a. modify   b. discharge   c. pursue   d. swindle

6. A person who freely expresses his or her opinion is _____.
   a. singular   b. economical   c. negative   d. frank

7. When you fire a gun, you _____ it.
   a. swindle   b. discharge   c. pursue   d. modify

8. A person who is careful about spending money is _____.
   a. frank   b. negative   c. economical   d. singular

9. A person who makes comments and suggestions that are not helpful
   is being _____.
   a. economical   b. negative   c. frank   d. singular

10. A willing accomplice to a robbery is a(n) _____ of the thief.
   a. confederate   b. alibi   c. discharge   d. mutiny

11. The anniversary celebration was the _____ event of the year.
   a. frank   b. singular   c. negative   d. economical

12. When you keep trying to achieve a goal, you _____ it.
   a. modify   b. discharge   c. pursue   d. swindle

Actors **pursue** their goal of becoming Broadway stars.

Synonyms

For each item below, choose the word that is most nearly the **same** in meaning as the word or phrase in **boldface**. Then write your choice on the line provided.

1. a **blunt** answer to your question
a. frank   b. negative   c. singular   d. economical   _____

2. revise the schedule
a. discharge   b. pursue   c. modify   d. swindle   _____

3. aim for a career in medicine
a. modify   b. discharge   c. swindle   d. pursue   _____

4. an ironclad **excuse**
a. confederate   b. reign   c. alibi   d. mutiny   _____

5. a **regime** of terror
a. swindle   b. discharge   c. mutiny   d. reign   _____

6. cheated by a con artist
a. pursued   b. swindled   c. modified   d. discharged   _____

Antonyms

For each item below, choose the word that is most nearly **opposite** in meaning to the word or phrase in **boldface**. Then write your choice on the line provided.

1. positive numbers
a. negative   b. singular   c. economical   d. frank   _____

2. the **wasteful** use of natural resources
a. frank   b. economical   c. singular   d. negative   _____

3. soldiers who **obey**
a. discharge   b. mutiny   c. reign   d. swindle   _____

4. load a cannon
a. modify   b. pursue   c. swindle   d. discharge   _____

5. plural nouns
a. negative   b. economical   c. singular   d. frank   _____

6. enemies of the tribe
a. reigns   b. alibis   c. mutinies   d. confederates   _____

Completing the Sentence

Choose the word from the box that best completes each item below. Then write the word in the space provided. (You may have to change the word's ending.)

alibi	confederate	discharge
economical	frank	modify
mutiny	negative	pursue
reign	singular	swindle

Editing An Essay

■ When I write an essay, I review what I have written to see how I can improve it. One way that I may _____ the essay is to get rid of any repetitions.

■ Because I want to keep the reader's attention, I try to keep my sentences clear and brief. Therefore, I look for more _____ ways to make my points.

■ For example, if I am writing about two people, I may want to use the plural pronoun *they* instead of _____ pronouns such as *he* and *she*.

Trouble on the High Seas

■ Captain William Bligh, an English admiral, _____ over his ship, the *Bounty*, as if he were its king.

■ His harsh treatment and mean-spirited rules aroused _____ feelings among crew members. Few viewed the captain in a favorable light.

■ In a secret but _____ discussion, the sailors plotted to take over the ship.

■ A ship's officer named Fletcher Christian seized control of the *Bounty* on April 28, 1789. This daring _____ has been the subject of several movies.

Crime at the Cash Machine

■ Soon after my uncle opened a checking account at a new bank, he was the victim of a bank machine _____.

■ A woman posing as a banker and her _____ advised my uncle to get $200 from the ATM to test his bank card. The crooks then ran off with the money.

■ Using the descriptions given by my uncle and a witness, the police _____ the two thieves on foot, catching up to them a few blocks away.

■ They soon arrested the suspects without having to _____ their weapons.

■ At their trial, the two thieves claimed that they were innocent. But the jury did not believe their _____. It took only fifteen minutes to find them guilty.

Word Associations

Circle the letter next to the word or expression that best completes the sentence or answers the question. Pay special attention to the word in **boldface.**

1. A **frank** comment is
   a. always complimentary.
   b. never hurtful.
   c. always appreciated.
   d. never dishonest.

2. An **economical** car probably
   a. stalls frequently.
   b. uses little gas.
   c. pollutes the air.
   d. runs on air.

3. Infantry soldiers who **mutiny** are likely to
   a. get medals.
   b. be promoted.
   c. get new uniforms.
   d. be punished.

4. To **modify** a drawing you might
   a. erase a few lines.
   b. crumple it up.
   c. show it to a friend.
   d. go to a museum.

5. Which of these is a good **alibi**?
   a. "I didn't do it."
   b. "I was in school at that time."
   c. "I saw them rob the store."
   d. "I hope you catch the crook."

6. Which of these is a **singular** noun?
   a. chicks
   b. geese
   c. goose
   d. ducks

7. A **negative** person is likely to
   a. take great vacation pictures.
   b. be good at math.
   c. find fault with any plan.
   d. see the best in everyone.

8. A **reigning** king probably has
   a. boots and an umbrella.
   b. a scepter and a crown.
   c. a computer and a modem.
   d. a bow and an arrow.

9. If I **swindle** my little brother, I
   a. cheat him.
   b. read to him.
   c. protect him.
   d. draw a picture of him.

10. A factory is likely to **discharge**
    a. prisoners.
    b. metal parts.
    c. rifles.
    d. smoke.

11. I would expect my **confederates** to
    a. work together with me.
    b. make fun of me.
    c. refuse to help me.
    d. plot against me.

12. Which of these is a cat most likely to **pursue**?
    a. a dream
    b. a mouse
    c. a dog
    d. a career in television

Word Study • Dictionary: Multiple-Meaning Words 2

You have learned that **multiple-meaning words** have more than one meaning. One example is *negative* (page 143). If you look up *negative* in a dictionary, you will find an entry with numbers showing the different meanings.

> **negative 1.** *(adj.)* saying no: *I gave a negative response to the party invitation.* **2.** *(adj.)* not positive or helpful: *A negative person may be overly critical of others.* **3.** *(n.)* a photographic image in which light and dark areas are reversed: *A photographer can print a picture from a negative.*

Read this sentence: *Someone who has a* **negative** *attitude may not be willing to try new things.* You can tell from the definitions that the sentence illustrates meaning 2 of *negative*.

Look at the chart to find other examples of multiple-meaning words.

barge	**1.** *(n.)* a flat-bottom boat used for moving things **2.** *(v.)* to enter or interrupt rudely
harvest	**1.** *(n.)* the crops picked from a field **2.** *(v.)* to gather crops, such as wheat, from a field
murmur	**1.** *(n.)* a low continuous sound **2.** *(v.)* to speak in a low voice

PRACTICE *Write the multiple-meaning word from the chart above that completes each sentence. Using the part of speech can help you choose the word. Then write the number of the meaning.*

_____ **1.** Why did you _____ into the room without knocking?

_____ **2.** The _____ of the air conditioner put me to sleep.

_____ **3.** The poor fruit _____ was due to the cold weather.

_____ **4.** The shy student seemed to _____ the answer.

APPLY *Complete each sentence so that it makes sense. Use the multiple-meaning word in* **boldface.** *You may have to change the word's ending.*

5. murmur If you need to talk in the library, _____.

6. barge Along wide rivers, _____.

7. harvest When the beans were ripe, we _____.

8. negative People won't want you on their team _____.

Search through newspapers, magazines, or books to find a sentence with one of the multiple-meaning words above. Write the sentence. Then write the meaning that is illustrated.

Shades of Meaning • Adages and Proverbs 2

In the passage "A Giant Hoax" on pages 140–141, many people who saw the Cardiff Giant believed it was real and paid money to see it. You might use this proverb or adage to describe the Cardiff Giant: **All that glitters is not gold.**

A **proverb** or **adage** is a short, well-known expression or saying that states an obvious truth or gives advice. *All that glitters is not gold* is a proverb. It cautions us that some things, such as the Cardiff Giant, are not always what they seem.

PRACTICE *Read each sentence. Decide which proverb best expresses a truth about the situation described. Write the number of the sentence next to the proverb.*

1. Instead of sitting and waiting for my friend to call, I kept busy by cleaning my room.

2. Each night, Dad put loose change in a jar. At the end of the month, he had twenty dollars.

3. I learned my routine well, but I just didn't want to perform it.

4. The batter was skinny and small for his age, so we were all surprised when he hit a home run.

_____ Don't judge a book by its cover.

_____ A watched pot never boils.

_____ You can lead a horse to water, but you can't make it drink.

_____ A penny saved is a penny earned.

APPLY *Write what someone might say to make you respond with each proverb below. The first one has been done for you.*

5. Appearances can be deceiving.

The restaurant looks run-down, but it has the best food in town.

6. Beggars can't be choosers.

_____

7. Half a loaf is better than none.

_____

8. Fool me once, shame on you. Fool me twice, shame on me.

_____

9. Bad news travels fast.

_____

UNIT 15

Introducing the Words

Read the following tall tale about a larger-than-life hero of the Old West. Notice how the highlighted words are used. These are the words you will be learning in this unit.

Pecos Bill Ends a Drought

(Tall Tale)

According to the tales that Texas cowboys used to tell, Pecos Bill was raised along the Pecos River by coyotes. That upbringing might have been a bit unusual, but it gave Bill superhuman powers.

Just about everything Pecos Bill did was a spectacle. He had a lariat as long as Texas, so he could rope a herd of cattle with just one throw. To keep those cattle safe, he decided to use New Mexico as his pasture. Fencing in that pasture would have complicated anyone else's life, but not Bill's. He just persuaded the prairie dogs to dig the postholes for him.

These stunts that Bill performed had universal appeal. Even the sun showed its curiosity, straining closer and closer to get a better look at whatever Bill was up to. That's what caused the great Texas drought. Never had the state been so dry before! The sun didn't mean any harm, but it got so close that it scorched the land. Every blade of grass dried up and turned brown because of the burning heat.

Talk about a hot summer! The heat was so severe that the chickens laid fried eggs. People wanted to cry and grieve, but there wasn't enough water for tears.

Pecos Bill felt the discomfort, too. After all, the tragic situation was partly his fault. A moral man, Bill always tried to do what was right. He was also a man of action, so he decided to end the drought.

Hopping onto his horse Widow-Maker, Bill galloped north across Oklahoma. Halfway up Tornado Alley, he spotted what he was looking for. A big, black twister had just torn up half of Kansas and was heading down toward Oklahoma for a repeat performance. Bill didn't hesitate for a second. Taking out his lariat, he roped the tornado and climbed onto its neck.

"Howdy, friend!" said Bill in his courteous way, looking directly into the eye of the storm. "I could use your help down in Texas."

"How dare this cowboy trifle with a tornado!" the twister snorted to itself. Bucking like a bronco, the big funnel-shaped cloud whirled, twirled, and zig-zagged south, hoping to throw Bill off. Bill held on, though, digging his spurs into the tornado's sides and riding it south. Past Galveston and out into the Gulf of Mexico, the twister spun, quickly filling with water.

That's just what Bill was planning. Full of water, the tornado slowed down a bit, allowing Bill to steer it west over Texas. There, with a few well-placed kicks, Bill turned the twister into a giant watering can.

Once the tornado had dropped all its water, it turned nasty again, so Bill rode it back to the Gulf for more. In all, Bill made six trips, bringing enough water to end the drought and eliminate the hardship he had caused.

Actually, only five trips would have been necessary. When Texans saw Bill coming back with his sixth load, they waved their hats and shouted, "No!" Any more water and they'd have a flood. In the end, Bill rode the twister over to Arizona and dumped all the water in one great swoosh, a washout that created the Grand Canyon.

Definitions

You were introduced to the words below in the passage on pages 150–151. Study the pronunciation, spelling, part of speech, and definition of each word. Write the word in the blank space in the sentence that follows. Then read the synonyms and antonyms.

1. complicate
(käm′ plə kāt)

(v.) to make hard to understand or do

A lot of unnecessary details can _____ *directions.*

SYNONYMS: to confuse, muddle, mix up
ANTONYMS: to simplify, clarify, smooth, ease

2. courteous
(kûr′ tē əs)

(adj.) considerate toward others

A _____ *host makes her guests feel welcomed.*

SYNONYMS: polite, well-mannered, respectful, civil
ANTONYMS: rude, impolite, ill-mannered, discourteous

3. discomfort
(dis kum′ fərt)

(n.) a lack of ease and well-being

A nasty case of chicken pox can cause a great

deal of _____.

SYNONYMS: pain, distress, irritation, suffering
ANTONYMS: comfort, peace, calm

4. eliminate
(i li′ mə nāt)

(v.) to get rid of or do away with

By working together, we can _____ *hunger and poverty.*

SYNONYMS: to remove, omit, leave out, exclude, drop
ANTONYMS: to take in, admit, acquire, retain, preserve

5. grieve
(grēv)

(v.) to cause to feel great sadness; to feel very sad

Reports of the many deaths and the destruction caused by the

earthquake _____ *us all.*

SYNONYMS: to sadden, mourn, regret
ANTONYMS: to rejoice, celebrate, gladden

6. moral
(môr′ əl)

(adj.) having to do with what is right and wrong; being good and just

A _____ *question is sometimes very difficult to answer.*

(n.) the lesson taught by a story or experience

I think that the _____ *of the story is "never give up."*

SYNONYMS: (adj.) honorable, upright, honest; (n.) a message, teaching
ANTONYMS: (adj.) immoral, wicked, bad, wrong

7. scorch
(skôrch)

(v.) to burn on the surface; to dry out with heat

Did you _____ my brand-new shirt with the iron?

(n.) a slight burn
I placed the napkin so it would cover a

_____ in the tablecloth.

SYNONYMS: (v.) to singe, brown, blacken, shrivel

8. severe
(sə vēr')

(adj.) of a serious nature; very strict and harsh; causing pain or hardship

Most parents think lying is a _____ offense.

SYNONYMS: grave, stern; tough, bitter; brutal, rough
ANTONYMS: unimportant; mild; merciful

9. spectacle
(spek' ti kəl)

(n.) an unusual sight or public display
Millions of people visit New York every year

to view the _____ of the Manhattan skyline.

SYNONYMS: a scene, show, exhibition, marvel

10. tragic
(tra' jik)

(adj.) having to do with a serious story with a sad ending; very unfortunate

Stories with _____ endings make me cry.

SYNONYMS: dreadful, awful, sad, disastrous, unhappy
ANTONYMS: amusing, funny, humorous, comical, happy

11. trifle
(trī' fəl)

(n.) something of little importance; a small amount

It is not worth arguing over such a _____.

(v.) to treat carelessly or playfully

It is unkind to _____ with someone's feelings.

SYNONYMS: (n.) a bit, knickknack, trinket; (v.) to fiddle, play, toy
ANTONYMS: (n.) a lot, lots of

12. universal
(yü nə vûr' səl)

(adj.) being everywhere; of, for, or shared by all

Food and shelter are _____ needs.

SYNONYMS: worldwide, broad, general, widespread
ANTONYMS: local, limited, narrow

Match the Meaning

vocabularyworkshop.com **Practice** unit words with interactive games and activities.

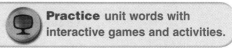

For each item below, choose the word whose meaning is suggested by the clue given. Then write the word in the space provided.

1. To feel great sadness over a loss is to _____.
a. scorch   b. trifle   c. grieve   d. eliminate

2. When you make a task harder, you _____ it.
a. complicate   b. eliminate   c. scorch   d. grieve for

3. If your throat is sore, you might feel _____.
a. moral   b. discomfort   c. scorch   d. spectacle

4. Joy that is shared by everyone in the world is _____.
a. tragic   b. severe   c. universal   d. moral

5. Someone who is considerate of other people's feelings is

_____.

a. courteous   b. moral   c. severe   d. tragic

6. During a dry spell the sun may _____ the earth.
a. complicate   b. eliminate   c. trifle with   d. scorch

7. A fatal accident is a _____ event.
a. moral   b. courteous   c. tragic   d. universal

8. A very strict or harsh king is a _____ ruler.
a. universal   b. severe   c. courteous   d. tragic

9. A life that is good and just is a _____ one.
a. moral   b. severe   c. tragic   d. universal

10. A small amount of something is a _____.
a. discomfort   b. moral   c. spectacle   d. trifle

11. To get rid of something is to _____ it.
a. complicate   b. grieve for   c. trifle with   d. eliminate

12. A visually striking display, such as a fireworks show, can be described as a

_____.

a. trifle   b. spectacle   c. discomfort   d. moral

It is **courteous** to cover your mouth when you cough.

Synonyms

*For each item below, choose the word that is most nearly the **same** in meaning as the word or phrase in **boldface**. Then write your choice on the line provided.*

1. caused great **distress**
   a. spectacle   b. trifle   c. discomfort   d. moral   _____

2. a grand **scene**
   a. moral   b. spectacle   c. trifle   d. discomfort   _____

3. the **message** of the fable
   a. trifle   b. scorch   c. spectacle   d. moral   _____

4. burned the grass
   a. scorched   b. eliminated   c. complicated   d. grieved for   _____

5. fiddle with the rules
   a. complicate   b. scorch   c. eliminate   d. trifle   _____

6. leave out the negative comments
   a. eliminate   b. complicate   c. trifle with   d. grieve for   _____

Antonyms

*For each item below, choose the word that is most nearly **opposite** in meaning to the word or phrase in **boldface**. Then write your choice on the line provided.*

1. simplify things
   a. scorch   b. complicate   c. eliminate   d. trifle with   _____

2. a **mild** winter
   a. severe   b. moral   c. universal   d. courteous   _____

3. having **limited** appeal
   a. tragic   b. severe   c. moral   d. universal   _____

4. amusing love stories
   a. universal   b. courteous   c. tragic   d. moral   _____

5. a **rude** customer
   a. severe   b. universal   c. courteous   d. tragic   _____

6. rejoice with the family
   a. trifle   b. grieve   c. scorch   d. eliminate   _____

Completing the Sentence

Choose the word from the box that best
completes each item below. Then write the
word in the space provided. (You may have
to change the word's ending.)

complicate	courteous	discomfort
eliminate	grieve	moral
scorch	severe	spectacle
tragic	trifle	universal

Death of a President

■ When President John F. Kennedy was killed by an assassin's bullet on November 22,

1963, the _____ event shocked the nation. The President was only
forty-five years old.

■ Americans _____ openly as they watched his formal state funeral on
television or listened to it on the radio.

■ People still recall the respectful and _____ behavior of the huge crowds
that lined the funeral route.

Why Save the Rain Forests?

■ The magnificent variety of animals and plants in the tropical rain forests creates a

_____ unlike anything else in nature.

■ The effort to protect these forests is _____ by the need to use some of
their valuable resources—for example, by using plants to make medicine.

■ When any plant or animal is forever _____ from the earth, the balance
of nature changes. The loss of a single species may result in harm to many more.

■ A change in the balance of nature can bring about a _____ shift in
weather patterns. A change that at first has only local effects may in time affect the
whole world.

■ Many people now regard destruction of the rain forests as a _____
issue, not just a political or legal one, because it can ruin the future of the entire planet.

Sunburn Really Hurts

■ Many people do not realize how easily they can _____ their skin just
by walking or playing outside on a sunny day.

■ Even on a cloudy day, it is possible to get a _____ sunburn.

■ If you get a painful sunburn, ask your doctor what you should do to ease the

_____.

■ Always remember that a sunburn is nothing to _____ with. It can
cause serious harm to your skin.

Word Study • Roots *spect, photo, tele*

Remember that a **root** is the main word part of a word. The root carries the meaning of the word. Knowing the meaning of a word's root can often help you figure out the meaning of the word.

Look at the chart to find the meanings of some words with the roots *spect, photo,* and *tele*.

spect—see
The root **spect** appears in **spectacle** (page 153). A **spectacle** is a sight that looks impressive or unusual.
photo—light
The root **photo** appears in **photography**. **Photography** is an art form that uses light to create pictures.
tele—far
The root **tele** appears in **telescope**. A **telescope** is a device used to see things that are far away.

spectator	someone who watches an event
prospect	something that is looked forward to or expected
photocopy	a copy of an image made by a process involving light
telegram	a message sent over wires to a distant place

PRACTICE *Complete each sentence with a word that contains the root spect, photo, or tele. Choose from the words above.*

1. Many students at the art school are studying _____.

2. I am excited by the _____ of getting a new bicycle.

3. Long before we had e-mail, people would send a _____.

4. One day, I hope to be a _____ at the Olympic Games.

APPLY *Complete each sentence to show you understand the meaning of the word in* **boldface.**

5. When I looked through the **telescope** last night, I saw _____.

6. The **spectacle** of holiday lights _____.

7. I made a **photocopy** of my science report _____.

8. The **prospect** of moving to a new city _____.

Write *Choose one of these roots: spect, photo, and tele. Create a word chain of three words, with each word containing the root. Here is an example: spect — inspect, inspector, inspection. Use a dictionary if you need help.*

Vocabulary for Comprehension

Read the following passage in which some of the words you have studied in Units 13–15 appear in **boldface.** *Then answer the questions on page 159.*

The Experience of a Lifetime

Ferris wheel on the grounds of the 1893 Chicago World's Fair

Carl, Anna, and their parents joined the crowd at the train station. They had prepared for this day since March. Carl earned money doing the morning milking. Anna baked pies and biscuits and sold them. The family had been very **economical,** saving every penny for the train tickets and the admissions fee. At last, the children and their parents were ready for the **singular** celebration of the century—the 1893 Chicago World's Fair. They joined travelers from all over the world who were eager to see the **spectacle** on Lake Michigan.

The train was nearly full when it entered the station. The crowd was quick to board. Anna clutched Carl's hand as Mom and Dad guided them toward a seat. After an hour's rattling ride, the train was at the fair's main gate.

Carl whistled. Anna gasped in awe. Tens of thousands of visitors were strolling the walkways. People toured halls packed with **exhibits.** Anna and Carl stopped to see a gigantic cheese from Canada. It weighed in at 22,000 pounds!

"C'mon, kids," Dad exclaimed. "Let's find the trained lions from Africa, the dishwashing machine, and the U.S. map that's made entirely of pickles!"

"First, the wheel," said Carl with enthusiasm.

"The wheel?" Anna asked.

"You know, the one by George Ferris, the genius engineer from Pittsburgh," Carl answered. "Maybe we can ride twice!"

The family headed toward the wondrous wheel, which towered over everything else. It was huge! Its 36 wooden cars carried 2,160 people high above the ground for a thrilling 20-minute view of the **sprawling** exhibition grounds. The ride had a **universal** appeal. People of all ages and nationalities waited in what seemed like an endless line. Carl and Anna joined the crowd and took their places in the long line for the ride of a lifetime.

Fill in the circle next to the choice that best completes the sentence or answers the question.

1. This passage was mainly written to
   (a) encourage tourism to Chicago.
   (b) provide a glimpse into the future.
   (c) describe the creation of the Ferris wheel.
   (d) provide a picture of the 1893 Chicago World's Fair.

2. The meaning of **economical** is
   (a) very wealthy.
   (b) self-centered.
   (c) reckless about spending money.
   (d) careful about spending money.

3. In this passage, **singular** means
   (a) disappointing.
   (b) exceptional.
   (c) ordinary.
   (d) short-lived.

4. A **spectacle** is a(n)
   (a) luxury boat.
   (b) grand public display.
   (c) dance performance.
   (d) impressive sunrise.

5. From the passage, you can tell that Carl and Anna live
   (a) on or near a farm.
   (b) in an apartment building.
   (c) in Chicago.
   (d) near Lake Michigan.

6. The **exhibits** in this passage are
   (a) paintings from an art class.
   (b) displays shown to the public.
   (c) preserves for wild animals.
   (d) amazing stories.

7. **Sprawling** most nearly means
   (a) narrow.
   (b) scenic.
   (c) spread out.
   (d) elaborate.

8. The meaning of **universal** is
   (a) very far away.
   (b) shared by all.
   (c) limited.
   (d) belonging to one person.

Write Your Own

Imagine that you are Carl or Anna. On a separate sheet of paper, write a journal entry about your day at the Chicago World's Fair. Include details that tell what you saw, heard, and did. Use at least three words from Units 13–15.

UNIT 16

Introducing the Words

Read the following journal article about huge animals that lived long ago. Notice how the highlighted words are used. These are the words you will be learning in this unit.

Why Did the Woolly Mammoths Disappear?

(Journal Article)

Before humans arrived in North America, giant-sized mammals walked the land. The best known were two elephant-like animals, the woolly mammoth and the mastodon. Less familiar is the short-faced bear, a rough and rowdy creature about thirty percent larger than today's grizzly. Sabre-toothed tigers, some weighing as much as 800 pounds, were a threat to any creature that trespassed in their territory. There were also giant wolves as well as camels, horses, and sloths. In terms of size, these creatures have no peers among the North American mammals of today.

The mega-mammals fared well on the continent for hundreds of thousands of years. At the beginning of the last ice age, about 130,000 years ago, the animals were still thriving. Even though ice covered much of the continent, the land was fertile enough to provide food.

Then, near the end of the ice age, something happened: The large mammals died off. It's impossible to give a rigid timetable for when these animals became extinct because these

extinctions happened too long ago. Yet at some point about 12,000 to 15,000 years ago, both the glaciers and many of the mammals seem to have disappeared rather suddenly, all at the same time.

For a long time, people assumed that the giant creatures had been hunted to extinction. The first human hunters had left Asia and wandered onto the North American continent about this time. Hunting with spears, the newcomers fanned out across the continent. As the colonies of humans expanded, the theory goes, they killed off many species.

Were there enough hunters to endanger so many species? Few archaeologists think so. Other facts also undercut this theory. For one thing, archeological sites are crammed with clues about what the early hunters killed and ate. Mammoths and mastodons were their favorites. Apparently, these people didn't hunt the other extremely large mammals. Yet these animals died off, too. Furthermore, the early people did hunt bison, but this species, of course, survived.

An exploding comet may have led to the extinction of the woolly mammoth.

Recently, scientists have furnished another explanation for the extinctions. A large comet, which is a traveling body of ice and dust, may have exploded on or just above Earth about 12,000 years ago. The clouds of dust from the disaster would have caused a long period of cooling on Earth. The cold temperatures would have led to the extinctions of dozens of species.

There is evidence for the comet theory. Arctic ice that formed about 12,000 years ago shows high levels of iridium, the element found in comets and meteorites. Also, tiny diamonds, called nanodiamonds, appear in soil samples dating from 12,000 years ago. The flash of the explosion could have formed them. This theory could explain why large mammal species would have died off so suddenly.

Many species, however, survived the disaster and cold climate. Among them are the wild animals that we're most familiar with today. Why were they safeguarded from the cooling while the larger species were not? By unraveling the history and mystery of ancient climate change, scientists hope one day to find the answer.

Woolly mammoths lived during Earth's last ice age.

Definitions

You were introduced to the words below in the passage on pages 160–161. Study the pronunciation, spelling, part of speech, and definition of each word. Write the word in the blank space in the sentence that follows. Then read the synonyms and antonyms.

1. assume
(ə sŭm′)

(v.) to take upon oneself; to pretend to have or be; to take for granted
My parents said I could have the puppy if I would

_____ *the responsibility for it.*

SYNONYMS: to accept, undertake, seize; to imagine, suppose, believe
ANTONYMS: to reject, refuse, give up

2. cram
(kram)

(v.) to stuff tightly; to fill tightly; to study hard just before a test

Mom told me not to _____
all my clothes into one drawer.

SYNONYMS: to pack, crowd, jam, load, squeeze
ANTONYMS: to empty, clean out, clear out

3. endanger
(in dān′ jər)

(v.) to expose to injury or harm

Fire and drought will _____ *the forest animals.*

SYNONYMS: to risk, threaten
ANTONYMS: to protect, defend, preserve, save, secure

4. fare
(fâr)

(v.) to get along

If you study hard, you should _____ *well in school.*

(n.) the cost of travel on public transportation; food and drink

We can't afford the plane _____ *to the East Coast.*

SYNONYMS: (v.) to manage, succeed; (n.) a charge, fee, price; a menu

5. fertile
(fûr′ təl)

(adj.) good for producing crops and plants; capable of growing
The Midwest's farms are located in one of the

most _____ *areas in the world.*

SYNONYMS: fruitful, productive, rich
ANTONYMS: barren, unproductive

6. furnish
(fûr′ nish)

(v.) to supply with furniture; to supply with what is needed

After the fire, neighbors helped to _____ *the new house.*

SYNONYMS: to equip, outfit, provide, give
ANTONYMS: to take, withhold

7. mammoth
(ma' məth)

(n.) a very large, long-tusked, shaggy-haired elephant, that is now extinct

No woolly _____ are alive today.

(adj.) great in size

A skyscraper is a _____ building.

SYNONYMS: (adj.) enormous, huge, immense, gigantic, colossal
ANTONYMS: (adj.) small, tiny, little, miniature

8. peer
(pēr)

(n.) a person of the same age, rank, or ability; a British noble

As a gifted pianist, the child had no _____.

(v.) to look closely at

I tend to _____ at people through my glasses.

SYNONYMS: (n.) an equal, colleague; (v.) to gaze, stare, scan

9. rigid
(ri' jəd)

(adj.) not bending; very strict

Stand at attention, and keep your body _____.

SYNONYMS: stiff, firm, inflexible; severe, stern
ANTONYMS: elastic, flexible, loose

10. rowdy
(rau' dē)

(adj.) rough and disorderly

My teacher does not tolerate _____ behavior.

SYNONYMS: wild, unruly, noisy
ANTONYMS: quiet, tame, gentle, mild

11. safeguard
(sāf' gärd)

(n.) something that protects

A helmet is a _____ against head injuries.

(v.) to protect against possible danger

Wear sunblock to _____ your skin.

SYNONYMS: (n.) a protection, defense; (v.) to defend, guard, save
ANTONYMS: (v.) to endanger, threaten, risk

12. trespass
(n., tres' pəs;
v., tres' pas)

(n.) an action that is wrong; unlawful entry onto someone's property

The man was charged with criminal _____.

(v.) to do wrong; to enter onto someone's property without right

I did not mean to _____ against you.

SYNONYMS: (n.) a sin, wrongdoing; an invasion; (v.) to sin, offend, intrude

Match the Meaning

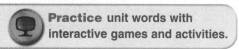

vocabularyworkshop.com **Practice** unit words with interactive games and activities.

For each item below, choose the word whose meaning is suggested by the clue given. Then write the word in the space provided.

1. If I put people at risk, I _____ their lives.
    a. cram   b. safeguard   c. assume   d. endanger

2. A noisy and wild party may be described as _____.
    a. mammoth   b. rowdy   c. fertile   d. rigid

3. A member of British royalty is a _____.
    a. peer   b. safeguard   c. mammoth   d. fare

4. To take something for granted is to _____ it is so.
    a. cram   b. assume   c. furnish   d. endanger

5. When I eat bread and cheese for lunch, I dine on simple

_____.

    a. safeguards   b. mammoths   c. fare   d. trespasses

6. A large, extinct "woolly" elephant is called a _____.
    a. mammoth   b. safeguard   c. peer   d. fare

7. If a lot of people get on a bus or train, they _____ into it.
    a. furnish   b. assume   c. safeguard   d. cram

8. A person who is very strict may be described as _____.
    a. rowdy   b. rigid   c. mammoth   d. fertile

9. If I protect people from risk, I _____ their lives.
    a. assume   b. endanger   c. safeguard   d. furnish

10. An egg that can develop into a chick is one that is _____.
    a. fertile   b. rowdy   c. mammoth   d. rigid

11. To enter someone's property without first getting permission is to

_____.

    a. cram   b. endanger   c. trespass   d. peer

12. If I supply necessary information, I _____ the facts.
    a. safeguard   b. endanger   c. assume   d. furnish

If people become **rowdy** in a restaurant, they might be asked to leave.

Synonyms

*For each item below, choose the word that is most nearly the **same** in meaning as the word or phrase in **boldface**. Then write your choice on the line provided.*

1. stare through the window
   a. cram   b. trespass   c. peer   d. assume   _____

2. rich soil
   a. rigid   b. fertile   c. rowdy   d. mammoth   _____

3. defend the planet
   a. furnish   b. endanger   c. cram   d. safeguard   _____

4. collect the **fee**
   a. mammoth   b. fare   c. safeguard   d. peer   _____

5. equip the lab
   a. furnish   b. endanger   c. cram   d. safeguard   _____

6. intrude on private property
   a. peer   b. assume   c. trespass   d. cram   _____

Antonyms

*For each item below, choose the word that is most nearly **opposite** in meaning to the word or phrase in **boldface**. Then write your choice on the line provided.*

1. small in size
   a. rigid   b. mammoth   c. rowdy   d. fertile   _____

2. a **quiet** activity
   a. rigid   b. fertile   c. mammoth   d. rowdy   _____

3. a **flexible** rule
   a. mammoth   b. rowdy   c. fertile   d. rigid   _____

4. empty your locker
   a. furnish   b. safeguard   c. cram   d. endanger   _____

5. protect the spotted owl
   a. cram   b. endanger   c. furnish   d. safeguard   _____

6. give up control
   a. furnish   b. safeguard   c. assume   d. endanger   _____

Completing the Sentence

Choose the word from the box that best completes each item below. Then write the word in the space provided. (You may have to change the word's ending.)

assume	cram	endanger
fare	fertile	furnish
mammoth	peer	rigid
rowdy	safeguard	trespass

A Big Mistake

■ I made a big mistake when I _____ that I could wait until the night before the big test to start studying.

■ My _____ teased me when I told them that I was worried about the test. They said I didn't need to study hard. I shouldn't have listened to them.

■ I had to stay up very late to _____ my brain full of facts and figures. When I realized how much I needed to learn, I began to feel sick with panic.

■ To make matters worse, the people in the house next door had a _____ party that lasted until one o'clock in the morning. I couldn't sleep because of the noise.

■ The next day I was so tired that I couldn't remember anything. So it was no surprise that I _____ badly on the test.

Save the Wetlands

■ America's wetlands provide a rich and _____ environment for thousands of species of plants and animals.

■ But pollution and development more and more _____ these beautiful places. In some areas their very survival is at risk.

■ If we lose our wetlands, many of the creatures that live there will become as extinct as the woolly _____.

■ Lots of concerned individuals and organizations are working to educate the public about how important it is to _____ this precious natural resource.

Safety in a Dangerous Place

■ Scientists who study deadly viruses work in special laboratories that have strict safety measures. There are _____ rules to protect all the employees.

■ All workers are _____ with special protective clothing that they must put on before going into the lab.

■ Only employees are allowed to enter the lab. Other people will be considered to be _____. Security guards will escort intruders from the building.

Word Associations

*Circle the letter next to the word or expression that best completes the sentence or answers the question. Pay special attention to the word in **boldface**.*

1. A **fertile** animal may give birth to
   a. many young.
   b. green plants.
   c. good ideas.
   d. fruits or vegetables.

2. A jury of your **peers** would be made up of
   a. two dukes.
   b. your parents.
   c. other students.
   d. telescopes.

3. A **rowdy** greeting is likely to be
   a. stern.
   b. loud.
   c. gentle.
   d. whispered.

4. Which is a **safeguard** against theft?
   a. a burglar alarm
   b. sunscreen
   c. lifeguard
   d. deodorant soap

5. Which usually requires paying a **fare**?
   a. a skateboard ride
   b. a taxi ride
   c. a car ride
   d. a sled ride

6. One who **assumes** a brave manner is
   a. bragging.
   b. fighting.
   c. shouting.
   d. pretending.

7. A **crammed** suitcase is probably
   a. well organized.
   b. half full.
   c. hard to close.
   d. locked.

8. One way to say "No **Trespassing**" is
   a. "Closed for Repairs."
   b. "Keep Out."
   c. "Out of Business."
   d. "This Way to Exit."

9. If I **furnish** food for a picnic, I
   a. invite the ants.
   b. set up the lawn furniture.
   c. eat the lion's share.
   d. bring lots to eat.

10. A **mammoth** corporation probably has
    a. a large board of directors.
    b. many elephants.
    c. lions, tigers, and bears.
    d. a small parking lot.

11. An **endangered** species is
    a. threatened by extinction.
    b. dangerous to others.
    c. safe from harm.
    d. protected by mammoths.

12. Which of these is **rigid**?
    a. a rubber band
    b. a mound of jello
    c. a soap bubble
    d. a steel beam

Word Study • Suffixes -ity, -ty, -ence, -al

Remember that a **suffix** is a word part that is added to the end of a **base word** to make a new word. When a suffix is added to a base word, the new word that is formed is often a different part of speech. You can add the suffix *-ity* to *rigid* (page 163) to make a new word.

> The suffixes **-ity, -ty,** and **-ence** mean "the act, quality, or state of." These suffixes form nouns.
>
> rigid *(adj.)* + **ity** = rigid**ity** *(n.)* ⟶ means "the state of being stiff"
> frail *(adj.)* + **ty** = frail**ty** *(n.)* ⟶ means "weakness"
> violent *(adj.)* + **ence** = viol**ence** *(n.)* ⟶ means "the use of force to create harm"
>
> The suffix **-al** means "relating to." This suffix forms adjectives.
> accident *(n.)* + **al** = accident**al** *(adj.)* ⟶ means "happening by chance or mistake"

PRACTICE *Write the missing base word, suffix, or new word. Then write the meaning of the new word. Use a dictionary to check your answers.*

Base Word	Suffix	New Word	Meaning
1. _____	+ ence	= absence	⟶ _____
2. real	+ _____	= reality	⟶ _____
3. topic	+ al	= _____	⟶ _____
4. _____	+ ty	= loyalty	⟶ _____

APPLY *Add a word for each missing part of speech. The word should be from the same word family. Use any suffix you know. The first one has been done for you.*

	Noun	Adjective
5. globe	globalization	global
6. prosper	_____	prosperous
7. person	personality	_____
8. music	musicality	_____

Speak Work with a partner to list words with the suffixes -ity, -ty, -ence, and -al. Then take turns asking and answering questions that include those words.

Example: **Q:** What is the noun form of *differ*?

A: difference

Shades of Meaning • Words That Describe Size

In the passage "Why Did the Woolly Mammoths Disappear?" on pages 160–161, you read about a large animal called the woolly **mammoth**. The word *mammoth* is also an adjective that describes size.

Look at the words in the chart. The words show a range of sizes, from very tiny to extremely large. When you describe the size of something, using the right word can help you communicate what you want to say.

mammoth	Something **mammoth** is huge and remarkable. It is almost unbelievable because of its size.
miniature	Something that is **miniature** is smaller than normal. The word is often used to describe a scale model.
microscopic	Something that is **microscopic** is so small that it can only be seen through a microscope.
vast	Something that is **vast** is very great in area, size, or amount.

PRACTICE *Write the word from the chart above that best completes each sentence.*

1. My parents set up the _____ train in the living room for my baby sister.

2. The scientist found _____ rug fibers in one of the samples.

3. The first computers were _____ compared to today's laptops.

4. In science class, we learned how _____ the universe is.

5. The model of the White House on my desk is _____ in size.

6. The museum has a _____ collection of antique pottery.

APPLY *List two items that can be described using each size word.*

7. **mammoth** _____, _____

8. **miniature** _____, _____

9. **microscopic** _____, _____

10. **vast** _____, _____

Introducing the Words

Read the following fable about a plan that backfires. Notice how the highlighted words are used. These are the words you will be learning in this unit.

The Hunger Strike

(an Aesop Fable)

Today, the parts of the body get along and work together surprisingly well, but that wasn't always true. Long ago, Head, Legs, and Arms had frequent squabbles with one another; there was a great deal of friction among them. One of the few things they had in common, in fact, was their dislike for Belly. Most of the time, they disregarded Belly completely and weren't even sure where he lived. When they did turn their attention to him, their main complaint was about his lack of purpose. They all agreed that Belly had never done an honest day's work and that he only cared about eating.

Thinking about Belly's laziness, Head eventually felt such profound anger that he called a meeting of the other body parts. "It's time to teach that lazy Belly a lesson!" he announced loudly. Legs and Arms couldn't agree more. They found the idea irresistible and immediately asked Head what he had in mind.

"Well, from now on," explained Head, "I'm not going to figure out any ways to find food." With his sharp eyes and quick brain, Head was the body part that found the majority of the body's food.

"Belly won't like that," remarked Legs with a smile. Then to show that he was in complete agreement with Head, he said, "And I promise not to walk over to any food, even if it's lying on the ground right in front of us."

"This is going to be good," giggled Arms, clapping his hands together for emphasis. "I won't pick up any food," he promised the others, "and I'm not doing any cooking either!"

All went according to plan, and after a few weeks of no food, Belly indeed was grumbling. "Please," he begged, "a crust of bread, anything."

The other body parts, however, could take no real joy in Belly's misery, for they were having problems themselves. Head, for example, experienced frequent dizziness. Then a new phenomenon—a splitting headache—made it impossible for him to think. Legs grew weaker and weaker, often stumbling into swamps and other desolate places. Even Arms, who was by now covered with sores from shoulders to fingertips, realized something was very wrong.

As the body's problems accumulated, Head had to intervene. He called the body parts to another meeting. "Even though Belly never seems to work," Head began, "he must have a purpose. Otherwise, starving him wouldn't

have caused us so many problems. For our own sakes, therefore, I suggest we compromise and start feeding him again."

Legs and Arms agreed with Head. They were greatly relieved that the standoff had come to an end. Without wasting another minute, the whole crew went out to find some dinner. Once the meal had been eaten, Belly's loud grumbling subsided, and the other body parts started feeling much better, too!

Moral: *Each member of a group must do his or her part for the common good.*

Definitions

You were introduced to the words below in the passage on pages 170–171. Study the pronunciation, spelling, part of speech, and definition of each word. Write the word in the blank space in the sentence that follows. Then read the synonyms and antonyms.

1. **accumulate**
   (ə kyü′ myə lāt)

   (v.) to gather together, often in an increasing number

   I hope to _____ a large collection of stamps.

   SYNONYMS: to collect, hoard
   ANTONYMS: to disperse, lessen, lose, spend

2. **compromise**
   (käm′ prə mīz)

   (n.) an agreement in which each side gives up some demand

   The battling senators reached a _____ and passed the bill.

   (v.) to give up certain demands in order to settle an argument

   I had to _____ and let my brother join our team.

   SYNONYMS: (n.) concession; (v.) to cooperate, settle
   ANTONYMS: (n.) confrontation; (v.) to confront

3. **desolate**
   (des′ ə lit)

   (adj.) bleak and without any people; extremely unhappy

   The abandoned gold rush town was

   _____.

   SYNONYMS: deserted, isolated, miserable
   ANTONYMS: populous, happy

4. **disregard**
   (dis ri gärd′)

   (v.) to pay no attention to

   I told my friend to _____ my earlier message.

   (n.) the state of ignoring something

   The driver who ran the red light showed _____ for the law.

   SYNONYMS: (v.) to ignore, neglect; (n.) contempt, indifference
   ANTONYMS: (v.) to heed, attend; (n.) concern, attention

5. **emphasis**
   (em′ fə sis)

   (n.) the special importance or value given to something; stress given to a syllable or word in reading or speaking

   Our school puts a strong _____ on science.

   SYNONYMS: prominence, weight; accent, stress

6. friction
(frik′ shən)

(n.) the rubbing of one object or surface against another; conflict

Tires wear down because of

_____ *between the*

rubber and the road.

SYNONYMS: rubbing, grating; discord, trouble
ANTONYMS: agreement, peace

7. intervene
(in tûr vēn′)

(v.) to come between things, points, events in order to make changes

The referee had to _____ *to settle the players' dispute.*

SYNONYMS: to interfere, intrude, meddle
ANTONYMS: to avoid, ignore

8. irresistible
(ir i zis′ tə bəl)

(adj.) too attractive and tempting to be resisted

A swimming pool on a hot summer day is _____.

SYNONYMS: alluring, desirable, enticing
ANTONYMS: avoidable, undesirable

9. majority
(mə jôr′ i tē)

(n.) the greater number

The _____ *of the puppies were black.*

(adj.) something made up of the greater number

The class president can be removed by a _____ *vote.*

SYNONYMS: bulk, mass, more
ANTONYMS: minority

10. phenomenon
(fə nom′ ə non)

(n.) something that can be taken in by the senses or mind; someone or something that is very unusual

Glaciers are a natural _____.

SYNONYMS: occurrence, spectacle, wonder, sensation, exception
ANTONYMS: normality, regularity

11. profound
(prə faůnd′)

(adj.) very great or intense; requiring deep thought or understanding

The family felt _____ *sadness at the loss of its pet.*

SYNONYMS: insightful, heartfelt, overpowering
ANTONYMS: superficial, trivial, shallow

12. subside
(səb sīd′)

(v.) to become less intense, violent, or severe

We waited for the rain to _____ *before going outside.*

SYNONYMS: to fall, lower, settle, decline
ANTONYMS: to increase, grow, rise

Match the Meaning

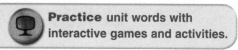

vocabularyworkshop.com **Practice** unit words with interactive games and activities.

For each item below, choose the word whose meaning is suggested by the clue given. Then write the word in the space provided.

1. Your teacher might _____ if she notices you are having difficulty with an assignment.
   a. accumulate   b. intervene   c. subside   d. disregard

2. A deserted beach on a cold, rainy day is likely to be _____.
   a. profound   b. irresistible   c. desolate   d. majority

3. When there is _____ between two people, they do not get along.
   a. compromise   b. phenomenon   c. emphasis   d. friction

4. As a hurricane loses strength, the winds begin to _____.
   a. disregard   b. accumulate   c. subside   d. intervene

5. Seeing an eclipse of the sun is a(n) _____ because it a rare occurrence.
   a. majority   b. phenomenon   c. friction   d. emphasis

6. Authors sometimes put words in boldface to show

   _____ or importance.
   a. phenomenon   b. emphasis   c. compromise   d. friction

7. Before you can build a snowman, a few inches of snow need to

   _____.
   a. subside   b. accumulate   c. compromise   d. intervene

8. When you _____ something, you pay no attention to it.
   a. accumulate   b. subside   c. intervene   d. disregard

9. A(n) _____ comment shows deep thought and understanding.
   a. majority   b. desolate   c. irresistible   d. profound

10. You can win an election if the _____ of people vote for you.
    a. friction   b. emphasis   c. majority   d. phenomenon

11. If something is too good to walk away from, it is _____.
    a. irresistible   b. profound   c. majority   d. desolate

12. When you _____ with someone, you reach an agreement with that person.
    a. intervene   b. compromise   c. accumulate   d. disregard

It's amazing
how much laundry
will **accumulate**
after vacation.

Synonyms

For each item below, choose the word that is most nearly the **same** in meaning as the word or phrase in **boldface**. Then write your choice on the line provided.

1. a **stress** on the syllable
   a. disregard   b. friction   c. emphasis   d. compromise _____

2. reaching an acceptable **settlement**
   a. phenomenon b. emphasis   c. friction   d. compromise _____

3. conflict between classmates
   a. compromise b. friction   c. emphasis   d. phenomenon _____

4. intrude in the argument
   a. intervene   b. subside   c. accumulate   d. disregard _____

5. once in a lifetime **spectacle**
   a. friction   b. phenomenon c. emphasis   d. compromise _____

6. gather a lot of money
   a. accumulate   b. compromise c. disregard   d. subside _____

Antonyms

For each item below, choose the word that is most nearly **opposite** in meaning to the word or phrase in **boldface**. Then write your choice on the line provided.

1. a **happy** expression
   a. irresistible   b. desolate   c. majority   d. profound _____

2. obey the rules
   a. compromise b. intervene   c. subside   d. disregard _____

3. an **undesirable** location
   a. majority   b. desolate   c. irresistible d. profound _____

4. a **minority** group
   a. irresistible   b. profound   c. desolate   d. majority _____

5. watching floodwaters **rise**
   a. accumulate   b. subside   c. intervene   d. disregard _____

6. a **trivial** idea
   a. profound   b. desolate   c. majority   d. irresistible _____

Completing the Sentence

Choose the word from the box that best completes each item below. Then write the word in the space provided. (You may have to change the word's ending.)

accumulate	compromise	desolate
disregard	emphasis	friction
intervene	irresistible	majority
phenomenon	profound	subside

The Sahara Desert

■ The Sahara Desert is a natural _____ that stretches across northern Africa in an area that is almost as big as the United States.

■ The central area of the desert is incredibly dry, _____, and famous for its seemingly endless sand dunes.

■ With the exception of the Nile River, the _____ of the rivers and streams in the Sahara flow only seasonally.

■ These sources of water rise in the rainy season and _____, or may even become completely dry the rest of the year.

■ Even in the parts of the desert that receive the most rain, no more than five inches of rain _____ each year.

■ In spite of the harsh conditions, some tourists find the adventure of the desert _____ and trek across the area on guided camel tours.

A Good Solution

■ Our school puts an _____ on athletics, and we are encouraged to play sports at recess.

■ Unfortunately, there was a great deal of _____ between the fourth and fifth graders about how to use the large ball field.

■ The fifth graders always used the entire field for soccer, and they showed _____ for the fourth graders who wanted to play kickball on the same field.

■ Eventually, the principal had to _____ because there was so much arguing at recess.

■ The principal said that we would have to reach a _____ that would allow both groups to enjoy the field.

■ Finally, a fourth grader said, "I think we should each play a shorter game and share the time on the field." We all thought that was a _____ statement.

Word Associations

*Circle the letter next to the word or expression that best completes the sentence or answers the question. Pay special attention to the word in **boldface**.*

1. You would feel the most **friction** when
  a. ice skating on smooth ice.
  b. painting a wall.
  c. using your feet to stop your bike.
  d. slicing a strawberry.

2. An **irresistible** person is most likely
  a. annoying.
  b. angry.
  c. boring.
  d. charming.

3. Your **profound** idea can make you feel
  a. clumsy.
  b. confident.
  c. confused.
  d. unprepared.

4. If your art class placed an **emphasis** on drawing, you would
  a. spend all of your time painting.
  b. spend little time drawing.
  c. spend the most time on drawing.
  d. not be allowed to draw.

5. Which sports story is a **phenomenon**?
  a. a gymnast scores a 10
  b. a baseball player strikes out
  c. a soccer player makes a goal
  d. a football player catches a pass

6. You would **intervene** in an argument
  a. to encourage the argument.
  b. to offer a solution to the dispute.
  c. by walking away from the situation.
  d. by not saying anything.

7. What might a **desolate** person say?
  a. "I'm determined to finish."
  b. "I can't wait to do this."
  c. "Things will get better soon."
  d. "I've never felt so terrible."

8. If you **disregard** a remark, you
  a. ignore it.
  b. respond to it.
  c. let it bother you.
  d. repeat it.

9. If the **majority** of students prefer math to science,
  a. more than half prefer science.
  b. more than half prefer math.
  c. science and math are liked equally.
  d. all the students prefer math.

10. What does a basketball player want to **accumulate**?
  a. points
  b. losses
  c. fouls
  d. injuries

11. To get a fever to **subside**, you might
  a. eat lunch.
  b. go for a run.
  c. sit in the sun.
  d. take medicine.

12. What might you say to **compromise**?
  a. "I'm not giving you anything."
  b. "Take it, or leave it."
  c. "I'm willing to make a deal."
  d. "I don't care what you want."

Word Study • Prefixes *de-*, *post-*, *trans-*, *sub-*

Remember that a **prefix** is a word part that is added to the beginning of a **base word** to make a new word. You can add the prefix *de-* to *emphasis* (page 172) to make a new word.

The prefix **de-** usually means "down." **de** + emphasis = **de**-emphasis → means "bring down in importance"
The prefix **post-** means "after." **post** + game = **post**game → means "after the game"
The prefix **trans-** means "across." **trans** + plant = **trans**plant → means "to move from one place to another"
The prefix **sub-** means "under" or "less than." **sub** + soil = **sub**soil → means "soil directly under the topsoil"

PRACTICE *Write the missing prefix, base word, or new word. Then write the meaning of the new word.*

Prefix	Base Word	New Word	Meaning
1. sub	+ _____	= subzero	→ _____
2. de	+ value	= _____	→ _____
3. post	+ _____	= postflight	→ _____
4. _____	+ atlantic	= transatlantic	→ _____
5. _____	+ frost	= _____	→ _____

APPLY *Complete each sentence with a word that contains the prefix* de-, post-, trans-, *or* sub-. *Choose from the words above.*

6. Traveling from New York to London requires a _____ flight.

7. I didn't want to _____ my action figure by taking it out of the box.

8. During the _____ show, the reporter will interview the winning team.

9. You must dress warmly to go out in _____ temperatures.

10. I will _____ the ivy from the smaller pot to the larger pot.

Speak *With a partner, list words with the prefixes* de-, post-, trans-, *and* sub-. *Take turns asking and answering questions that include those words.*

Example: Q: How is a *submarine* different from a typical military ship?

A: A submarine is a type of ship that can go underwater.

Shades of Meaning • Idioms 2

In the passage "The Hunger Strike" on pages 170–171, the parts of the body are used as characters to tell the story. The parts of the body are used in some idioms, too.

Remember that an **idiom** is an expression with a meaning that is different from the meaning of the words that make up the idiom. Here is an example: *When I took two helpings of potatoes, my **eyes were bigger than my stomach.*** Here, the idiom *eyes were bigger than my stomach* has nothing to do with the size of one's eyes or stomach. Instead, the expression means "wanting or taking more food than one can eat."

PRACTICE *Read each sentence. Figure out the meaning of each idiom in **boldface**. Write the number of the sentence next to the meaning of the idiom.*

1. My teacher said she **had her eye on** me after I whispered to my friend.

2. Yesterday, I told my friend about my problem. It felt good to **get it off my chest.**

3. Before it was my turn to sing, I had **butterflies in my stomach.**

4. At the end of the year, I was **up to my ears in** homework.

_____ feel nervous

_____ watching someone very carefully

_____ to be very busy with something

_____ tell something that has been bothering you

APPLY *Read each sentence. Figure out the meaning of each idiom in **boldface**. Write the meaning on the line provided.*

5. He **did not have a leg to stand on** because there was so much evidence against him.

_____

6. When the umpire made a bad call, I **lost my head** and threw my glove.

_____

7. My dad said our new car **cost an arm and a leg.**

_____

8. I really **put my foot in my mouth** when I told her what I really thought about her bad haircut.

_____

Introducing the Words

Read the following biography about a leader who developed a writing system to help people communicate. Notice how the highlighted words are used. These are the words you will be learning in this unit.

Sequoyah, Advocate of His People

(Biography)

The Cherokee (cher' ə kē) were an eastern woodland people whose original territory spread across a significant portion of the Southeastern United States. Many Cherokee villages had thirty to sixty homes built around a large meeting house known as a council house. At the center of each village was a town square where people gathered for dances, games, and ceremonies.

Sequoyah (si kwoi' ə) was born in a Cherokee village in Tennessee around 1770. At that time, white colonists were moving onto Cherokee land, often signing treaties to do so. The Cherokee people, however, had no written language, only a spoken one, and they could not read English. This was a fundamental problem because the spoken promises of the white settlers often contradicted the legal terms of the treaties.

As a young man, Sequoyah moved to Georgia, perhaps to escape the white settlers.

Sequoyah

There he became a skilled silversmith. His ignorance of written English, however, prevented him from signing his craft items like other craftspeople.

During the War of 1812, Sequoyah, like many Cherokees, joined the American army. While on duty, Sequoyah often watched white soldiers reading battle orders as well as letters from their families.

Before the war, Sequoyah had begun his preliminary work on developing a Cherokee system of written communication. Now he turned his attention to this challenge. First, Sequoyah listened carefully to spoken Cherokee. Over time, he extracted 85 or 86 basic sound-syllables from his observations. Every Cherokee word is some combination of these syllables. Sequoyah next assigned one symbol to each sound-syllable. He borrowed some symbols, such as Roman numerals, and made up others. He also retained a few letters from English. By 1821, Sequoyah had completed his work. The Cherokees adopted his concept of representing sounds in the Cherokee language as written symbols.

An advocate of education, Sequoyah personally taught the written language to hundreds of Cherokees. He also publicly demonstrated the results of his efforts. No one could have anticipated the success of written Cherokee. In a short time, thousands of Cherokees learned to read and write.

In 1828, the Cherokee people began to publish their own newspaper. It was called the *Cherokee Phoenix*, and it is still printed today. The Cherokee also used their new language to write a constitution. This document helped them form their own government—the Cherokee Nation. The constitution described the internal workings of this government.

Sequoyah believed that reading and writing would help the Cherokee hold on to their land. Sadly, this premise proved to be untrue. According to the terms of the 1828 Indian Removal Act, all native Americans had to give up their land and move west of the Mississippi. Between 1838 and 1839, an estimated 17,000 Cherokees were forced to move to Oklahoma. About 4,000 people died on this terrible trip, causing the Cherokee to call it the Trail of Tears.

In Oklahoma, the Cherokee faced another challenge. They had to learn how to survive in a new and different place. To do this, they depended on their written constitution and laws. They published important information in their newspaper. Written communication helped the people adjust to a new way of life.

Sequoyah's Cherokee writing system

Cherokee Alphabet.

Definitions

You were introduced to the words below in the passage on pages 180–181. Study the pronunciation, spelling, part of speech, and definition of each word. Write the word in the blank space in the sentence that follows. Then read the synonyms and antonyms.

1. advocate
(n., ad′ və kit;
v., ad′ və kāt)

(n.) a person who publicly supports a cause; a lawyer

I am an _____ of animal rights.

(v.) to be or speak in favor of

They _____ using computers in the classroom.

SYNONYMS: (n.) defender, supporter; (v.) to recommend, support
ANTONYMS: (n.) critic, enemy, opposition; (v.) to attack, criticize

2. anticipate
(an tis′ ə pāt)

(v.) to think of ahead of time

We _____ there will be a large crowd at the book signing.

SYNONYMS: to expect, assume
ANTONYM: to doubt

3. concept
(kän′ sept)

(n.) a general idea

The _____ of time travel interests me.

SYNONYMS: idea, notion

4. contradict
(kän trə dikt′)

(v.) to say the opposite of; disagree with

The calls of the referees _____ each other.

SYNONYMS: to challenge, confront, deny, differ
ANTONYMS: to accept, agree, confirm

5. extract
(v., ek strakt′;
n., ek′ strakt)

(v.) to remove or take out

The dentist decided to _____ my decayed tooth.

(n.) something drawn out of a natural substance, often used for flavoring

I like to add vanilla _____ to cookie batter.

SYNONYMS: (v.) to detach, disconnect, remove; (n.) excerpt

6. fundamental
(fun də men' təl)

(adj.) forming a foundation, basic

This country gives all its citizens _____ rights.

(n.) a basic part, principle, fact, or skill

Knowing how to add is a _____ of mathematics.

SYNONYMS: (adj.) basic, essential, important; (n.) basis, foundation, rule
ANTONYMS: (adj.) additional, extra, unnecessary; (n.) addition, extra

7. ignorance
(ig' nər əns)

(n.) a lack of knowledge or information

I felt embarrassed by my _____ of American history.

SYNONYMS: dumbness, simplicity
ANTONYMS: intelligence, brilliance, knowledge

8. internal
(in tûrn' əl)

(adj.) of or located within something

The _____ parts of a kiwi look very different from its hairy outside.

SYNONYMS: inner, inside, interior
ANTONYMS: external, outer

9. preliminary
(pri lim' ə ner ē)

(adj.) coming before a main event or activity

I made _____ notes before I wrote my speech.

SYNONYMS: introductory, initial, first
ANTONYMS: conclusion, final, closing

10. premise
(prem' is)

(n.) a statement upon which an argument or conclusion is based

The _____ of my argument is that all students should take art class.

SYNONYMS: assumption, idea, foundation

11. retain
(ri tān')

(v.) to continue to have; to hold or keep in

A cactus can _____ water inside its thick stem.

SYNONYMS: to remember, contain, save
ANTONYMS: to lose, release

12. significant
(sig nif' i kənt)

(adj.) having importance; notable

There was _____ damage after the storm.

SYNONYMS: important, considerable, noteworthy
ANTONYMS: insignificant, trivial, unimportant, minimal

Match the Meaning

vocabularyworkshop.com **Practice** unit words with interactive games and activities.

For each item below, choose the word whose meaning is suggested by the clue given. Then write the word in the space provided.

1. If you remember a fact, you _____ it.
   a. advocate   b. contradict   c. anticipate   d. retain

2. The _____ of an argument is its basic idea.
   a. premise   b. ignorance   c. extract   d. advocate

3. If you _____ a longer school day, you support the idea.
   a. contradict   b. advocate   c. extract   d. anticipate

4. A skill that you need in order to do something is called

   a(n) _____.
   a. fundamental   b. advocate   c. premise   d. ignorance

5. To _____ someone is to say something that the person would not agree with.
   a. extract   b. anticipate   c. contradict   d. advocate

6. People who have no knowledge about a subject may reveal their

   _____.
   a. ignorance   b. fundamental   c. concept   d. premise

7. To _____ a splinter is to remove it.
   a. contradict   b. advocate   c. extract   d. anticipate

8. An electric car was once a new _____ in car design.
   a. premise   b. extract   c. concept   d. ignorance

9. A(n) _____ amount of money is large, or considerable.
   a. fundamental   b. significant   c. internal   d. preliminary

10. To _____ something is to see it coming.
    a. retain   b. anticipate   c. extract   d. advocate

11. A(n) _____ injury may affect the organs in your body.
    a. preliminary   b. fundamental   c. significant   d. internal

12. A(n) _____ race is a contest you have to win before the final race.
    a. significant   b. fundamental   c. internal   d. preliminary

To be a really good basketball player, you must master the **fundamentals** of dribbling.

Synonyms

For each item below, choose the word that is most nearly the **same** in meaning as the word or phrase in **boldface**. Then write your choice on the line provided.

1. challenge the evidence
   a. contradict   b. advocate   c. extract   d. anticipate   _____

2. basic dance steps
   a. internal   b. fundamental   c. preliminary   d. significant   _____

3. remove unwanted pieces
   a. anticipate   b. advocate   c. contradict   d. extract   _____

4. a strange **notion**
   a. ignorance   b. concept   c. advocate   d. fundamental   _____

5. save the receipts
   a. extract   b. retain   c. anticipate   d. contradict   _____

6. a weak **assumption**
   a. premise   b. advocate   c. fundamental   d. ignorance   _____

Antonyms

For each item below, choose the word that is most nearly **opposite** in meaning to the word or phrase in **boldface**. Then write your choice on the line provided.

1. an **enemy** of the cause
   a. fundamental   b. advocate   c. premise   d. ignorance   _____

2. knowledge about physics
   a. fundamental   b. premise   c. ignorance   d. advocate   _____

3. minimal amount of time
   a. significant   b. fundamental   c. internal   d. preliminary   _____

4. closing remarks
   a. fundamental   b. internal   c. preliminary   d. significant   _____

5. doubt it will rain
   a. contradict   b. advocate   c. extract   d. anticipate   _____

6. appealing **external** qualities
   a. fundamental   b. preliminary   c. internal   d. significant   _____

Completing the Sentence

Choose the word from the box that best completes each item below. Then write the word in the space provided. (You may have to change the word's ending.)

advocate	anticipate	concept
contradict	extract	fundamental
ignorance	internal	preliminary
premise	retain	significant

Olive Oil

■ Many nutritionists say that including olive oil in your diet can have

_____ health benefits.

■ This _____ is based on findings that olive oil contains a special kind of fat that may help prevent heart disease.

■ The Greeks have been making olive oil for thousands of years, so using it in meals is

not a new _____.

■ In fact, the process of obtaining an olive's _____ oil has not changed much since ancient times.

■ The _____ step in making olive oil is to grind the olives into paste.

■ Then the paste is placed in a press, where the oil is _____.

The Right To Vote

■ Susan B. Anthony, who lived from 1820 to 1906, was an _____ for American women.

■ She challenged the _____ of people who believed that women did not deserve the same rights as men.

■ Susan B. Anthony argued that women should be granted _____ rights, such as the right to own property, to have a job, to earn equal pay, and to vote.

■ Susan B. Anthony voted in the 1872 Presidential election. Her action

_____ the law that protected the voting rights of adult male citizens in that year.

■ Despite her arrest and jailing two weeks later, Susan B. Anthony _____ her belief in the cause of women's rights.

■ She _____ that her trial would eventually result in granting women the right to vote. Unfortunately, the Nineteenth Amendment, which provides that right, was not passed until 1920.

Word Study • Roots *dict*, *tract*

Remember that a **root** is the main word part of a word. It carries the meaning of the word. Knowing the meaning of common word roots, such as *dict* and *tract*, can often help you figure out the meanings of words with those roots.

Look at the chart to find the meanings of some words with the roots *dict* and *tract*.

dict—say
The root **dict** appears in **contradict** (page 182). To **contradict** what someone said is to deny or say the opposite.
tract—pull, draw
The root **tract** appears in **tractor**. A farm **tractor** can pull a wagon filled with grain.

dictate	to say or read aloud something for someone to write down or record
predict	to say what will happen
attract	to pull toward itself; to draw attention by creating interest
retract	to draw or pull something back in

PRACTICE *Complete each sentence with a word that contains the root* dict *or* tract. *Choose from the words above.*

1. When you read, you can _____ how a story will end.

2. A magnet will _____ metal items, such as paper clips.

3. A teacher will _____ spelling words to the students.

4. If something you touched were very hot, you would _____ your hand.

APPLY *Answer each question using a complete sentence to show you understand the meaning of the word in* **boldface.**

5. Why might you **retract** something you said?

_____

6. What do you **predict** the weather will be like tomorrow? Why?

_____

7. What sentence might your teacher **dictate** to you to **attract** your attention?

_____

Work with a partner to list other words that contain the roots dict *and* tract. *Write definitions for the words. Then consult a dictionary, either in a book or online, to check the meanings.*

Vocabulary for Comprehension

*Read the following passage in which some of the words you have studied in Units 16–18 appear in **boldface**. Then answer the questions on page 189.*

The Great Migration of the Dust Bowl

For many families in the American Great Plains, the 1930s was a time of great hardship. Even though the region had become known for its **fertile** land, a severe drought during this time period created dangerous conditions for families living there. Certain farming practices had damaged layers of grass that held the soil in place. When the drought caused the earth to dry, the soil blew about easily. As the dried soil blew and **accumulated**, huge dust clouds formed and spread across large areas of land, resulting in massive dust storms. This **phenomenon** and the region in which it occurred became known as the *Dust Bowl*.

The Dust Bowl had a **significant** impact on a large part of the country. Between 1930 and 1936, thousands of acres of land were affected by the dust storms. While states such as Texas, Oklahoma, and Kansas saw the worst damage, at times, the dust rolled as far east as New York City. The conditions **endangered** the lives of many Americans. The dust was so thick and the wind was so fierce that farms became useless and thousands of people were left without homes.

Many people had no choice but to leave the area and move further west. The trek across the country was long and difficult. Many travelers struggled to find **fundamental** necessities, such as food and water. Some people died from lung conditions brought on by the dust. Some died of starvation. This migration of people during the time of the Dust Bowl was one of the largest in American history. More than two million people had moved West by 1940, and many of them settled in California.

Eventually, the land recovered, but only after people learned to change how they farmed. New government programs were established, and farmers were taught better practices that would serve to protect the soil.

Fill in the circle next to the choice that best completes the sentence or answers the question.

1. This passage was mainly written to
   (a) describe farming practices in the Great Plains.
   (b) inform readers about the Dust Bowl.
   (c) encourage readers to move West.
   (d) instruct farmers on how to protect soil.

2. In this passage, the meaning of **fertile** is
   (a) barren.
   (b) desolate.
   (c) fruitful.
   (d) unhealthy.

3. In this passage, the meaning of **accumulated** is
   (a) gathered together.
   (b) subsided.
   (c) decreased in amount.
   (d) became less of a problem.

4. The meaning of **phenomenon** is
   (a) a common problem.
   (b) a normal experience.
   (c) a rare event.
   (d) an ordinary incident.

5. The Dust Bowl had a **significant** impact because it
   (a) was quickly forgotten.
   (b) was a minor event in history.
   (c) greatly affected many people and events.
   (d) occurred in the Great Plains.

6. The meaning of **endangered** is
   (a) threatened.
   (b) ensured.
   (c) aided.
   (d) encouraged.

7. Another word for **fundamental** is
   (a) essential.
   (b) unimportant.
   (c) extra.
   (d) worthless.

8. Which of the following best describes the Great Plains during the Dust Bowl period?
   (a) fertile
   (b) hearty
   (c) neutral
   (d) desolate

Write Your Own

During a severe dust storm, the air often became so thick with dry soil that it could block out the sun. Imagine that you are living in Kansas during the Dust Bowl period. On a separate sheet of paper, write a letter to relatives in California, informing them about what life is like for you. Use at least three words from Units 16–18.

Classifying

Choose the word from the box that goes best with each group of words. Write the word in the space provided. Then explain what the words have in common.

achievement	contradict	desolate
extract	ignorance	latter
mammoth	monotonous	moral
reign	rigid	severe

1. honest, trustworthy, reliable, _____

_____

2. saber-toothed tiger, _____, dinosaur

_____

3. monotone, monotony, _____

_____

4. deserted, barren, bleak, _____

_____

5. beginning, middle, _____

_____

6. ignore, _____, ignorant

_____

7. equipment, _____, settlement, payment

_____

8. spice, seasoning, _____

_____

9. mild, moderate, _____

_____

10. rain, rein, _____

_____

11. predict, dictator, dictation, _____

_____

12. stiff, firm, inflexible, _____

_____

REVIEW UNITS 13–18

Completing the Idea

Complete each sentence so that it makes sense. Pay attention to the word in **boldface.**

1. The doctor will **discharge** me from the hospital when _____.

2. To **modify** your diet, you can _____.

3. It is **courteous** to say "thank you" when _____.

4. If you **cram** too many things in a drawer, _____.

5. In order to reach a **compromise**, we _____.

6. One cause that I **advocate** is _____.

7. To **preserve** left-over food, you should _____.

8. A **negative** person is more likely to _____.

9. I feel **discomfort** when I _____.

10. **Rowdy** fans at a sports game may _____.

11. One food that I find **irresistible** is _____.

12. A good coach will **intervene** when _____.

13. **Sanitary** conditions in a kitchen help prevent _____.

14. I would like to **pursue** a career in _____.

15. The **tragic** story ended with _____.

16. A **majority** of students in our school want _____.

17. After the **preliminary** round of competition, our team _____.

Writing Challenge

Write two sentences using the word **fare.** *In the first sentence, use* **fare** *as a verb. In the second sentence, use* **fare** *as a noun.*

1. _____

2. _____

Word List

The following is a list of all the words taught in the units of this book. The number after each entry indicates the page on which the word is first introduced.

abandon, 18
abolish, 100
absurd, 110
abuse, 120
accomplish, 58
accumulate, 172
achievement, 132
acquire, 132
advocate, 182
aggressive, 38
alibi, 142
alternate, 80
anticipate, 182
apparent, 58
appeal, 100
appliance, 120
assault, 18
associate, 38
assume, 162
avalanche, 110

barrier, 70
blemish, 48
bluff, 28
blunder, 8
blunt, 48
brisk, 90
brittle, 100

calculate, 70
cancel, 8
capable, 48
capacity, 58
cautious, 28
cherish, 90
civilian, 58
classify, 110
complicate, 152
compose, 70
compromise, 172
conceal, 58
concept, 182
conclude, 48
condemn, 100
confederate, 142
confirm, 120

considerable, 70
considerate, 90
consist, 28
continuous, 8
contradict, 182
convert, 18
courteous, 152
cram, 162

daze, 120
debate, 132
deceive, 38
demolish, 80
deputy, 70
descend, 100
desolate, 172
despise, 28
detect, 48
dictator, 101
discharge, 142
discomfort, 152
displace, 90
dispute, 18
disregard, 172
distribute, 8
document, 8
downfall, 90
duplicate, 58

economical, 142
eliminate, 152
emigrate, 38
emphasis, 172
endanger, 162
energetic, 80
enforce, 80
ensure, 110
estimate, 90
exhibit, 132
expand, 101
extract, 182

famine, 101
fare, 162
fatigue, 49
feat, 80
fertile, 162
festive, 49

flexible, 38
flimsy, 120
foe, 132
fragile, 9
frank, 142
friction, 173
fundamental, 183
furnish, 162

gauge, 121
glamour, 39
grieve, 152

haven, 28
hazy, 39
hearty, 81
hospitality, 49
humiliate, 91

identical, 91
ignorance, 183
impressive, 18
improper, 91
industrious, 70
internal, 183
intervene, 173
irresistible, 173

jolt, 71
justify, 19

keen, 59

latter, 133
linger, 39
loot, 71
luxurious, 39

majority, 173
mammoth, 163
massacre, 133
mature, 81
migrant, 121
miniature, 29
mishap, 39
misleading, 19
modify, 142
monarch, 29

monotonous, 133
moral, 152
mutiny, 143
myth, 9

navigate, 110
negative, 143
nestle, 111
neutral, 121
nomad, 49
numerous, 19

observant, 81
obstacle, 29
overwhelm, 39

peer, 163
persecute, 49
phenomenon, 173
pitiless, 121
plea, 111
poll, 91
portable, 101
postpone, 29
preliminary, 183
premise, 183
presentable, 121
preserve, 133
prey, 101
primary, 81
principle, 111
productive, 19
profound, 173
provoke, 59
pursue, 143

realistic, 111
reign, 143
reject, 9
rejoice, 71
reliable, 71
resign, 81
retain, 183
rigid, 163
rotate, 121
rowdy, 163

safeguard, 163
sanitary, 133
scorch, 153
scuffle, 9
security, 111
selective, 111
senseless, 71
severe, 153
shred, 121
shrewd, 19
shrivel, 71
significant, 183
singular, 143
solitary, 9
soothe, 91
span, 39
spectacle, 153
sprawl, 133
spurt, 59
straggle, 29
strategy, 19
strive, 81
subside, 173
supreme, 49
swindle, 143

tart, 111
temporary, 9
thrifty, 101
tragic, 153
transport, 49
treacherous, 29
trespass, 163
trifle, 153

undoing, 59
universal, 153

vast, 59
verdict, 81
veteran, 9
vicinity, 91
villain, 19
visual, 101
vivid, 29

widespread, 133
withdraw, 59